Immortality, Resurrection
and the
Age of the Universe:
A Kabbalistic View

Immortality, Resurrection and the Age of the Universe: A Kabbalistic View

by
Aryeh Kaplan

With an Appendix:
Derush Or ha-Hayyim
by Rabbi Israel Lipschitz
(translated and annotated by Yaakov Elman)

KTAV Publishing House, Inc.
Hoboken, NJ

in Association with
Association of Orthodox Jewish Scientists
New York, NY

Library of Congress Cataloging-in-Publication Data

Kaplan, Aryeh.
    Immortality, resurrection, and the age of the universe / by Aryeh
Kaplan : with an appendix Derush Or ha-Hayyim by Israel Lipschitz :
translated and annotated by Yaakov Elman.
        p.   cm.
    ISBN 0-88125-345-6
    1. Resurrection (Jewish theology) 2. Immortality—Judaism.
I. Lipschutz, Israel ben Gedaliah, 1782-1860. II. Elman, Yaakov.
III. Title. IV. Title: Derush Or ha-Hayyim.
BM645.R47K37 1992
296.3'2—dc20   92-36917
                                                                      CIP

Manufactured in the United States of America

Contents

Foreword

Less than forty years ago, the very notion of an Orthodox Jewish scientist was still considered an anomaly on the Jewish scene. Today the religiously observant doctor, engineer, and psychologist are called upon by the rav, or Torah authority, to explain the scientific principles that will guide him in his halakhic decision-making. Rabbis, faced with the need to apply the Halakhah to a rapidly changing technological world, find it easier to communicate their needs to Torah scholars who are equally well versed in the sciences. The Orthodox Jewish scientist has indeed come a long way in the synthesis of Torah and science. Einstein's special and general relativity principles, proven reliable by the Haefele-Keating time-dilation experiments, "Big Bang," and string theory have all underscored the words of Hazal: *hafokh bah ve-hafokh bah de-khula bah* ("review it over and over, for all is in it").

The Association of Orthodox Jewish Scientists has always been at the interface between Halakhah and the emerging new technologies, and has been in the forefront of meeting the challenge to faith posed by modern scientific discoveries. With semiannual conventions, conferences, and lectures, the *Proceedings of the Association of Orthodox Jewish Scientists*, *Intercom*, and its monthly newsletter, the AOJS has helped Torah-committed physical scientists and engineers, health care professionals, and behavioral scientists address the real, everyday halakhic concerns of the Orthodox Jewish community. The Orthodox Jewish scientist, working through the AOJS, has become a major resource of reliable scientific information for the Torah community all over the world, and is recognized as having made important contributions in very practical ways to the development of the Halakhah. In line with this practice, the Association of Orthodox Jewish Scientists is proud to pub-

lish four previously unpublished manuscripts by the late Rabbi
Aryeh Kaplan, of blessed memory.

Rabbi Kaplan, a creative and prolific thinker and writer, who
during his short lifetime contributed so much to the revitalization
of Judaism in America and the world, was particularly interested
in problems raised by modern cosmological theories. The title essay of this collection, "The Age of the Universe," was delivered by
Rabbi Kaplan as a lecture at the Association's 1979 winter conven-
tion. Though saddened by Rabbi Kaplan's untimely death, we are
happy to help perpetuate his memory and his ideas through this
publication.

The Association acknowledges Mrs. Toby Kaplan Seidenfeld
for making her husband's manuscripts available to us. I would like
to thank Dr. Yaakov Elman for undertaking the task of editing the
manuscripts, and for translating and annotating the *Derush Or ha-
Hayyim* by Rabbi Israel Lipschitz. And *acharon acharon haviv*, I
would like to thank Dr. Neil Maron, president of the Association of
Orthodox Jewish Scientists, for realizing the importance of this
project. I am grateful for his confidence in me, and for his encour-
agement, without which this book would not have been completed.

Judah Mansbach
Managing Editor
Publications Committee
Association of Orthodox Jewish Scientists

Preface

We live in an age of sophisticated science in which many Torah practicing Jews have achieved prominence. It is therefore surprising and disappointing that so relatively few have used their scientific knowledge, talent, and prestige to demonstrate and argue the absence of a contradiction between their lives as scientists and as Torah Jews. This is especially true at a time when the explosive expansion of scientific knowledge has so challenged the way scientists view the universe, that each day the gap between science and faith grows smaller. The past few years has seen many physicists, biologists, and astronomers discover faith, convinced that the universe is the product of design and mind, not chance and happenstance. The new tools of science reveal a degree of complexity and incredible ingenuity so manifest in the design of even the simplest organisms that the thinking of many has changed.

Rabbi Aryeh Kaplan and the AOJS have both played a key role in bringing the message of the legitimate role Torah plays in the world of science to the attention of wide audiences.

Rabbi Kaplan was original, creative, resourceful, and courageous. He was prepared to express views which were tentative and controversial; he had a unique grasp of Torah in all its facets and an uncanny ability to discover unpublished texts authored by the greats of previous generations. He believed that scientific knowledge was the handmaiden of Torah and that by exploring both he could reveal the greatness of Torah as well as the wisdom of the Creator and Master of the universe. He optimistically anticipated that the advance of scientific knowledge would demolish the anti-Torah views of many. Sometimes, instead of setting forth his own view he would rely on the unpublished texts he had discovered through his unending research.

ix

Only a person of sterling reputation, towering scholarship, and exceptional stature could have undertaken to write on topics so sensitive and controversial. Above all Aryeh Kaplan was a searcher after truth, who lived the conviction that in the final analysis truth is Torah. Because he was the master of both Torah and science he saw harmony in the meeting of both worlds while others either compartmentalized their lives into two hermetically sealed worlds or drifted from one world to the other, denigrating the one as they abandoned the other.

Who else but Rabbi Aryeh Kaplan possessed the magic touch with which to make complicated, mystical, philosophical, religious concepts come to life with clarity, simplicity and force. Only he was able to lower his pail deep into the wellsprings of our tradition, deeper than had been done in the English language until his time, to bring us refreshing and revealing Torah insights.

A person of great sincerity, persistence, drive and staying power, he had that rare ability to lock himself in his room and work around the clock for days on end until he solved a problem or produced a highly original manuscript.

Religious concepts are often difficult to understand, and for many are elusive and unattainable. Rabbi Kaplan possessed the rare ability to bring them into focus. He had the special gifts and talents which make it possible to connect science to Torah, philosophy to action, mysticism to logic. He knew how to take abstract concepts and give them life. He had the talent to restore faith, to bring God's living message to our hearts and minds. Despite the fact that he was a deep and distinguished scholar, a rare talmid hakham who had mastered all branches of Torah wisdom, he possessed the common touch; he understood how people think and was able to convey deep and complicated concepts in everyday language.

I first encountered this extraordinary individual when by "chance" I spotted his article on "Immortality of the Soul" in *Intercom*, the journal of the Association of Orthodox Jewish Scientists, and was taken by his unusual ability to explain a difficult topic, one usually reserved for advanced scholars, a topic almost untouched in English, with such simplicity that could be understood by any intelligent reader. It was clear to me that his special talent could fill a significant void in English Judaica.

A soft-spoken, unassuming individual, modest despite his spreading renown and popularity, Aryeh Kaplan was a firm believer in acquainting unaffiliated and alienated Jewish youth with their heritage.

He was a prime mover behind the teshuvah movement, the modern movement of return to Jewish observance. "Throughout history, Jews have always been observant," he noted in an interview. "The teshuvah movement is just a normalization. The Jewish people are sort of getting their act back together again. We are just doing what we are supposed to be doing." Indeed, his books reflect a similar, upbeat philosophy. The message he tried to get across was that "Judaism is a live growing concern. A person looking for meaning in life need not go anywhere else."

Aryeh Kaplan's unusual warmth, sincerity and total dedication to Torah were an inspiration to the thousands he reached personally. His home was always open, his table crowded with Sabbath guests and students. He traveled far and wide to share his knowledge and commitment with young people at seminars, retreats and college campuses.

Rabbi Aryeh Moshe Eliyahu ben Shmuel Kaplan abandoned a promising career in physics, deciding instead to devote himself totally to the dissemination of Torah. He succeeded in uniting many elements in one personality, he was the Talmudic sage, the man of Halakhah, the master of Western civilization, and the scientist, with an uncanny grasp of Kabbalah, Jewish mysticism and Hassidic thought.

In the process of bringing Torah to the masses, Rabbi Kaplan revealed much that was previously hidden. His mind contained libraries of books, waiting to be put into writing. It was the will of the Lord that so much be revealed and no more.

Rabbi Pinchas Stolper
Executive Vice-President
Union of Orthodox Jewish Congregations of America

Chapter 1
The Age of the Universe

The question of the age of the universe has been discussed in Torah circles for more than a century. The Torah seems to teach that the universe is no more than six thousand years old. Indeed, many would say that any opinion stating that the world is more than six thousand years old must of necessity contradict the Torah. However, there appears to be a great deal of observational evidence that the universe is much older than six thousand years.

A number of approaches have been proposed to resolve this problem, some of which were discussed in a book published a few years ago.[1] Our concern, however, is not merely to resolve the question, but to do so in a manner firmly based on Torah teachings. That is to say, we seek a solution that is actually found in the classical Torah literature.

Methodological Principles

Before we can even begin to try to resolve this problem, we must lay down a few methodological principles. The first is the most important. We must be fully aware of what the primary sources say about the issue. Unfortunately, people often put forth their own ideas as Torah principles, claiming the authority of the classical sources for notions to which they are diametrically opposed.

Second, we must keep in mind that there is no one binding opinion in matters that do not involve Jewish law or fundamental matters of faith. One must always come to a final conclusion on a question of halakhah, since one must know how to act, but in regard to a non-halakhic question, such as the age of the universe, any opinion found in a *recognized* Torah source is acceptable.

This principle is alluded to in a number of Talmudic passages. For example, the Talmud refrains from rendering a final opinion on questions involving Messianic times and tables the matter by categorizing it as a *hilkhatha le-meshiha*, "a law pertaining to the Messiah." Where there is no practical consequence, a final verdict need not be rendered.

Another example is the Talmud's use of the expression "Both are the words of the living God." This phrase appears in two places, once in a non-halakhic context and once with regard to the halakhic disputes between the School of Hillel and the School of Shammai.

In the former case, the Talmud does not provide a final verdict (*pesak*), while in the latter it concludes: "the law follows Hillel's School." Again, on non-halakhic issues, there need not be a final verdict.

Intellectual Corners

In trying to resolve an issue as basic as the age of the universe, it is important not to paint oneself into an intellectual corner. Once the community has taken a stand on an issue—even an erroneous stand—backing down from it is difficult.

One example that immediately comes to mind is that of the existence of extraterrestrial life. Around a decade ago, a number of prominent rabbis expressed the opinion that belief in any life beyond the earth was tantamount to heresy. I recall writing an article in *Intercom* refuting this idea and demonstrating how giants like Saadiah Gaon had felt that life on other worlds was totally consonant with Torah teachings. What many contemporaries were decrying as heresy was actually a totally acceptable Torah opinion.

Another example would be the question of whether the universe is geocentric or heliocentric. Very few of even the most conservative Torah Jews today would say that belief in a heliocentric universe goes against Torah teachings. But in the very recent past, there were many who maintained that belief in a geocentric world was essential to Judaism.[2]

I also recall that some thirty years ago, back when I was in yeshiva, there was a discussion about sending a rocket to the moon. A prominent rabbi staunchly maintained that according to Torah teachings there was no way in which this could be possible. His arguments were impeccable—but of course, wrong. It is very dangerous to paint oneself into an intellectual corner.

Possible Approaches

The danger is apparent in any discussion of the age of the universe, since the question of the world's age is fundamental to any discussion of science and Judaism. If this issue remains unresolved, science and Torah will remain constantly at loggerheads.

The simplest approach is to ignore the problem. I know an Orthodox biology professor who in synagogue staunchly maintains that the world is less than six thousand years old, but in class teaches the standard scientific chronology. It is as if he had one belief system when among Orthodox people and another when among his professional colleagues. This may be the easiest way out, but it is obviously not a satisfactory approach.

Another approach is taken by the many Orthodox Jews who maintain that science in general is a fraud—largely because of this very issue. For those who hold this view, the moral shortcomings of scientists are taken as evidence of their intellectual dishonesty. However, this too is a totally unsatisfactory approach, as would be evident to anyone even remotely connected with organized science.

Two popular solutions take the problem on squarely.

The first assumes that each day of creation was really millions, or even billions, of years long. The six days of creation, according to this viewpoint, represent the billions of years that the universe took to develop.

There are a number of difficulties with this approach, not the least being that there is no hint of it anywhere in the classical Torah literature.

Another approach is to assume that the universe was created with its "history" as one of its elements. Thus, when God created trees, He created them with rings that seem to indicate that they had an extensive past existence. A scientist living in the first centuries of creation, so the argument goes, would have been able to discuss the "weather conditions" that existed before creation on the basis of the rings of larger trees. (Closely related to this is the question as to whether or not Adam had a navel.)

If trees could have been created with an apparent history, then so could the rest of the universe. Every creature's genes contain evidence of its ancestry, but the genes would have been created with this "history." Fossils and ancient-looking geological formations could also have been created no more than six thousand years ago. Even the uranium used for radiocarbon dating could have been created with characteristics that would make it seem billions of years old.

One problem with this approach is that it makes the Creator appear to have perpetrated a fraud. If it is heresy to believe that the world is more than six thousand years old, why would God have created the world in such a manner that an honest observer would be led to a false opinion? This is all the more serious an objection in light of the midrash that states, "There is no falsehood in the works of creation."[3] The above theory seems to make all of creation an act of falsehood.

Furthermore, the argument is arbitrary. If God could have created a universe with a history six thousand years ago, then He also could have done so five minutes ago. There is no question but that an omniscient God could have created us with all our memories, as well as with records and histories going back thousands of years. But then, with an omnipotent God, every-thing, no matter how illogical, is possible. Still, we generally as-sume that God gave us reason and created the world in such a manner that it could be understood by the human mind.

Of course, we are all aware that these objections can be re-solved. The argument that the world was created with a history is impossible to refute, and if one feels comfortable with it, well and good. However, many might feel that it is an argument that approaches intellectual dishonesty and sophistry, as well as one which might create more problems than it resolves.

But there is an even more serious problem. Nowhere in To-rah literature is there even the barest hint of such an approach. If not for scientific discoveries, no one would have even thought about presenting such an argument. Thus, it is both *ex post facto* and without basis in the Torah.

Actually, this approach was first postulated by a gentile sci-entist a few years before Darwin published his theory of evolu-tion. At the time, scientists looked upon it as being a silly argu-ment—even before Darwin. It does not seem any more convinc-ing today.

There is another issue that must also be dealt with squarely. Many fundamentalist Christian groups have adopted the idea of creationism, a teaching based on the literal interpretation of the Bible. Of course, since gentiles do not take the Oral Torah into consideration, their approach is certain to be very differ-ent than ours. Moreover, many of their arguments have been very effectively refuted by some of the best scientific minds. That Orthodox Jews should align themselves with such groups is both dangerous and anti-Torah.

Sabbatical Cycles

The only choice remaining is to look into our classical To-rah literature and determine whether there are any pertinent statements regarding the age of the universe. Significantly, there is a very important, though not well known, concept that is discussed in the *Sefer ha-Temunah*, an ancient Kabbalistic work attributed to the first-century tanna, Rabbi Nehunya ben ha-Kanah. The work discusses the forms of the Hebrew letters and is the source of many of the most frequently cited opinions on this subject in the halakhic literature. Thus, *Sefer ha-Temunah* is not an obscure, unimportant work, but one which is relied upon by most halakhic authorities.

The *Sefer ha-Temunah* speaks about Sabbatical cycles (*shemitot*). This is based on the Talmudic teaching that "the world will exist for six thousand years, and in the seven-thousandth year, it will be destroyed."[4] The *Sefer ha-Temunah* states that this seven-thousand-year cycle is merely one Sabbatical cycle. However, since there are seven Sabbatical cycles in a Jubilee, the world is destined to exist for forty-nine thousand years.

There is a question as to which cycle we are in today. Some authorities maintain that we are currently in the second Sabbatical cycle.[5] Others maintain that we are currently in the seventh cycle.[6] According to the second opinion, the universe would have been forty-two thousand years old when Adam was created. As we shall see, the implications of this are very important.

Before going any further, it must be mentioned that most of the more recent Kabbalistic texts do not make any reference to these teachings. This is because two of the greatest recent Kabbalists, Rabbi Moses Cordovero (the RaMaK) and Rabbi Isaac Luria (the Ari) disputed this concept in general. Thus, the author of *Vayek'hel Mosheh* writes, "We can see the greatness of the Ari, since there was an opinion (regarding Sabbatical cycles) that was accepted by all the early Kabbalists, but was refuted by the Ari."[7]

Here, however, the second principle that was discussed earlier comes into play. Since this is not a matter of law, there is no binding opinion. Although the Ari may have been the greatest of Kabbalists, his opinion on this matter is by no means absolutely binding. Since there were many important Kabbalists who upheld the concept of Sabbatical cycles, it is a valid, acceptable opinion.[8]

According to *Sefer ha-Temunah*, then, there were other worlds before Adam was created. These were the worlds of previous Sabbatical cycles.

Significantly, there are a number of allusions to this approach in the Midrash. Thus, commenting on the verse, "It was evening and it was morning, one day" (Genesis 1:5), the *Midrash Rabbah* states, "This teaches that there were orders of time before this."[9]

Another well-known Midrashic teaching also appears to support the concept of Sabbatical cycles. The Midrash states that "God created universes and destroyed them."[10] One of the important classical Kabbalistic works, *Ma'arekhet Elokut*, states explicitly that this passage refers to worlds that existed in Sabbatical cycles before Adam was created. The same source states explicitly that the Midrashic teaching that "there were orders of time before this [creation]" is also speaking of earlier Sabbatical cycles.[11]

A Talmudic passage seems to support this view of Sabbatical cycles. According to the Talmud, and some Midrashim as well, there were 974 generations before Adam.[12] The number is derived from the verse, "Remember forever His covenant, a word He commanded for a thousand generations" (Psalms 105:8). This would indicate that the Torah was destined to be given after one thousand generations. Since Moses was the twenty-sixth generation after Adam, there must have been 974 generations before Adam. The *Ma'arekhet Elokut* states explicitly that these generations existed in the Sabbatical cycles before Adam's creation.

The concept of pre-Adamic cycles was well known among the Rishonim (early authorities), and is cited in such sources as Bahya, Recanati, Ziyyoni, and *Sefer ha-Hinnukh*.[13] It is also alluded to in the *Kuzari*, and in the commentaries of the Ramban and Ibn Ezra.[14]

Tif'eret Yisrael

One of the most recent authorities to speak about the concept of Sabbatical cycles is Rabbi Israel Lipschitz, the author of *Tif'eret Yisrael* on the Mishnah. At the end of the section of Nezikin he includes an essay entitled *Derush Or ha-Hayyim.* Since this work speaks of earlier creations, and of human beings existing before Adam, it was extremely controversial. Indeed, it was omitted from some editions of the commentary (and torn out of others!). Moreover, because of the *Derush,* a number of Hasidic groups do not use the *Tif'eret Yisrael* at all.[15]

One of the problems with the *Derush* is that the author does not cite all the sources. His most important sources are Ibn Ezra, the Ramban, and Bahya, which are also among the most ambiguous, especially if one has not actually seen the presentation in the original source, *Sefer ha-Temunah.*

Rabbi Lipschitz's approach is very interesting. He cites the Kabbalistic idea of universes existing before Adam and then concludes, "See how the teachings of our Torah have been vindicated by modern discoveries."[16] He then cites such discoveries as a mammoth found near Baltimore, as well as dinosaurs. Since such creatures no longer exist, they obviously lived during previous Sabbatical cycles.

He goes on to say that mountain ranges like the Himalayas (mentioned by name) were obviously formed by great upheavals. He concludes that these were the upheavals mentioned explicitly in *Sefer ha-Temunah,* and that this is a further vindication of Torah teachings. This statement is very significant. Nowadays, many people in the Torah world feel threatened by geological and paleontological discoveries. They regard dinosaurs and other fossils as problems that can only be resolved with great difficulty. Here, on the other hand, one of the leading Torah figures of the last century takes an entirely different approach, seeing these discoveries as upholding an important Torah teaching. While many Orthodox Jews today feel that they must challenge every scientific statement regarding pale-

ontology or geology, the author of *Tif'eret Yisrael* saw such discoveries as supporting Torah concepts.

Rabbi Isaac of Akko

The *Sefer ha-Temunah* establishes the age of the world, at
least according to some classical interpretations, at forty-two
thousand years. That is, the world was forty-two thousand years
old when Adam was created. This teaching was subject to a
highly significant interpretation by Rabbi Isaac of Akko (1250–
1350).

Rabbi Isaac of Akko was a student and colleague of the
Ramban, and one of the foremost Kabbalists of his time. He is
quoted often in Rabbi Elijah de Vidas' great musar classic, *Reshit
Hokhmah.* The Zohar was published in his lifetime, and he is
renowned as the individual who investigated (and verified) its
authenticity.

Several years ago, as part of a research project, I obtained a
photocopy of one of Rabbi Isaac's important works, *Ozar ha-
Hayyim.*[17] In it I discovered an entirely new interpretation of
the concept of Sabbatical cycles.[18]

Rabbi Isaac of Akko writes that since the Sabbatical cycles
existed before Adam, their chronology must be measured, not
in human years, but in divine years. Thus, the *Sefer ha-Temunah*
is speaking of divine years when it states that the world is forty-
two thousand years old. This has some startling consequences,
for according to many Midrashic sources, a divine day is 1,000
earthly years long, and a divine year, consisting of 365¼ days,
is equal to 365,250 earthly years.

Thus, according to Rabbi Isaac of Akko, the universe would
be 42,000 x 365,250 years old. This comes out to be 15,340,500,000
years, a highly significant figure. From calculations based on
the expanding universe and other cosmological observations,
modern science has concluded that the Big Bang occurred approximately 15 billion years ago. But here we see the same figure presented in a Torah source written over seven hundred
years ago!

I am sure that many will find this highly controversial. However, it is important to know that this opinion exists in our classical literature; moreover, that one of the most important Kabbalists of seven centuries ago calculated the age of the universe and came to the same conclusion as modern science. As the author of *Tiferet Yisrael* would have said, modern cosmological studies vindicate our approach to the Torah (as opposed, say, to the fundamentalist approach).

Fitting It in with the Torah

We must now ask how this fits in with the text of the Torah. Where in the Torah do we find any hint of these 15 billion years, or, indeed, any place in which to fit them? Basically, there are two approaches. The first is that of the *Ma'arekhet Elokut,* a work which we referred to above. According to this source, the Torah is silent about events that took place during the period when the earth was "chaos and void" (*tohu va-vohu*). Thus, the period of "chaos and void" mentioned in the Torah would have lasted 15 billion years.

The difficulty with this approach is that the seven days of creation would then have taken place no more than six thousand years ago. This would pose some of the same questions that were originally raised.

There is, however, another approach, alluded to in the Talmud and Midrash.

One of the puzzles in the Torah involves the two accounts of creation. The first account is recorded in Genesis 1:1-2:3, the second in Genesis 2:4-23. Several discrepancies between these two versions are noted in the Talmud and the Midrash.

Thus, in the first version, the Torah says, "God created man in His image, in the image of God He created him, male and female He created him" (Genesis 1:27). This would appear to indicate that man and woman were created simultaneously. On the other hand, the second version states explicitly that Eve was created from Adam's rib. The Talmud raises this question and then explains that God created man and woman simultaneously in thought, but created Adam first and Eve from his rib in actual deed. The two accounts in Genesis conform to these two acts of creation.[19]

An early commentary employs this concept in resolving a halakhic contradiction. In the Talmud there is a question as to whether the world was created in Tishrei or Nissan. The Talmud states that with regard to legal matters, we abide by the opinion that the world was created in Nissan.[20] This has practical consequences, such as the fact that *Birkat ha-Hamah* (the blessing over the sun) is recited in Nissan rather than in Tishrei. Yet the Talmud states explicitly that on Rosh Hashanah we say, "This day is the beginning of Your works," because we follow the opinion that the world was created in Tishrei.

The difficulty is noted by Tosafot, which states in the name of Rabbenu Tam that in Tishrei the world was created in thought, while in Nissan it was created in deed.[21] Significantly, even the Ari upholds the concept that there were two creations, one in thought and the other in deed.[22]

It would appear, then, that the seven days of creation described in the Torah actually occurred in thought rather than in deed. Of course, God's thoughts are not the same as ours, and it is possible to say that creation in thought actually refers to the creation of the spiritual counterparts of the physical world. This approach is found in a number of Hasidic sources.[23]

Thus, it may be that the seven days of creation took place over 15 billion years ago, before the Big Bang. This represented the creation of the spiritual infrastructure of the universe, which the Talmud refers to as "creation in thought." The universe then developed according to God's plan, guided by the spiritual infrastructure He had created. Finally, less than six thousand years ago, God created Adam as the first of a new type of being. Although human beings may have existed before Adam, he was the first to acquire a special spiritual sensitivity and be able to commune with God (see below, pp. 114-116).

There is an allusion to a separate creation in thought in Rashi's commentary. Rashi states that the name *Elokim* is used in the first account of creation because it *arose in thought* to create the world with the attribute of Justice. Not till later did God employ the Tetragrammaton, indicating that the attribute of Mercy was also in effect. It is significant, however, that the name *Elokim* is used throughout the entire first account of creation. Some Hasidic sources also associate the "creation with justice" with the worlds that were "created and destroyed."[24] The *Sefer ha-Temunah* states explicitly that the first Sabbatical cycle was one of unmitigated justice.

There is another pertinent Midrashic teaching, based on the tradition that whenever a Torah section begins with the expression "and these" (*ve-eleh*), it is a continuation of the preceding section, while when it begins with "these" (*eleh*) alone, it represents a break from the preceding section.

The Midrash notes that the second account of creation (Genesis 2:4) begins with the expression "these" rather than "and these." Therefore, says the Midrash, this account is not to be associated with what is described in the verses that come before it, since the preceding account deals with "chaos and void."[25] The Midrash unequivocally speaks of the seven days of creation as being "chaos and void."

Conclusion

As this discussion demonstrates, classical Torah sources not only maintain that the universe is billions of years old, but present the exact figure proposed by modern science. There are two accounts of creation in the Torah, the first speaking of the spiritual infrastructure of the universe, which was completed in seven days. This took place some 15 billion years ago, before the Big Bang. The second account speaks of the creation of Adam, which took place less than six thousand years ago.

What is most important is that there is no real conflict between Torah and science on this most crucial issue. If anything, Torah teachings are vindicated by modern scientific discoveries.

Appendix

Selections from Ozar ha-Hayyim, pp. 86b-87b

אהיד״ע (אני הצעיר יצחק דמן עכו) ראיתי לכתוב סוד גדול שראוי
להעלימו מאד. דע כי יומו של הקב״ה אלף שנה שלנו שני כי אלף שנה
בעיניך כיום. ושנתנו שס״ה ימים ורביע יום. א״כ השנה של מעלה הם
ג׳ מאות אלף שנה וחמשת אלפים שנה ור״נ שנה שלנו. ושנתים של
מעלה הם ז׳ מאות אלף שנה וכ״ה אלף שנה ות״יק שנים שלנו. מעתה
צא וכפול צא וכפול עד מ״ט אלף שנה, שכל שנה ג׳ מאות וס״ה יום
ורביע יום, וכל יום של מעלה הוא אלף שנה שלנו כמ״ש ונשגב ה׳ לבדו
ביום ההוא מי ימלל גבורת ה׳. בשכמל״ו. וכל זה כמש״ה אמנם ציורו
כפלי כפלים אלפי אלפי אלפים אינם בעיניו חשובים רגע. וייוצרו הוא
צ״ע (צדיק עליון). אמנם עם אין סוף די לך שתאמי אין סוף.

I, the insignificant Isaac of Akko, have seen fit to record a great mystery that should be kept very well hidden. One of God's days is one thousand years, as it is written, "For a thousand days in Your sight are as a day" (Psalms 90:4). Since one of our years is 365¼ days, a year on high is 365,250 of our years. Two years on high is 730,000 of our years. From this, continue multiplying to 49,000 years, each year consisting of 365¼ days, and each supernal day being one thousand of our years, as it is written, "God alone will prevail on that day" (Isaiah 2:11). "Who can speak of God's greatness?" (Psalms 106:2). Blessed be the name of Him whose glorious Kingdom is forever and ever.

All this relates to what the Scripture states. However, no matter how many times this picture is doubled, even thousands upon thousands, it would not even be like a second to [God].... However, with regard to the Infinite One, it is enough that He is called Infinite.

13

וראיה ברורה על קיום העולם שנים רבות מאד שילאה הלב לחשוב
אותם הוא מאמר ישעיהו הנביא ע"ה שאמ' הנער בן מאה שנה ימות
שכשם שאנחנו אומרים עכשיו על תינוק בן ג' שנים או בן פחות תינוק
מת כן נאמ' לעתיד לבא על איש שחי מאה שנה ומת תינוק מת לרוב
השנים שיחיה אדם. ואם יבואו קטני אמנה להכחיש ענין זר זה אמור
לו ואשר להיות כבר היה שמתושלח חי אלף שנה פחות ל' שנה. וודאי
האיש אשר חי ק' שנה ומת בימיו של מתושלח אמי' מתושלח עליו
תינוק קטן מת.

There is clear proof that the world has existed for many years from the verse in Isaiah, "A child, one hundred years old, shall die" (Isaiah 65:20). Today, if a child younger than three years old dies, we say that a baby has died. In the ultimate future, if a hundred-year-old man should die, we will say that a baby has died, because of the extreme longevity people will then enjoy. If people of little faith reject this strange matter, tell them that it has already happened, since Methuselah lived thirty years less than a millennium. Certainly, in the time of Methuselah, a person who died at one hundred years old would have been considered to have died very prematurely.

הנה עינינו רואות שקיום העולם ארוך מאד להוציא מלבם של האומרים
שאין קיומו בלתי מ"ט אלף שנה שהם ז' שמיטות.

Behold, our eyes see that the world has existed for a very long time. This is to refute the opinion of those who say that the world has not existed more than forty-nine thousand years, which is seven Sabbatical cycles.

NOTES

1. See Aryeh Carmell and Cyril Domb, eds., *Challenge: Torah Views on Science and Its Problems* (New York: Association of Orthodox Jewish Scientists, 1976, pp. 132-135).

2. See *Ma'amar Mevo ha-Shemesh,* printed together with *Sefer ha-Tekhunah* by Rabbi Hayyim Vital.

3. *Tanna deBe Eliyahu Zuta* 3, and see *Yalkut Shimoni* I, r. 1.

4. Sanhedrin 97a.

5. See *Derush Or ha-Hayyim,* translated and annotated in the appendix.
6. See *Livnat ha-Sapir.*
7. *Vayak'hel Mosheh,* introduction.
8. It is significant that the Radbaz (Rabbi David ibn Abi Zimra) was among those who upheld the concept of Sabbatical cycles. He also wrote *Magen David* as a commentary on *Sefer ha-Temunah.* Although the Radbaz was most famous for his responsa (*she'elot u-teshuvot*), he was also an important Kabbalist. Indeed, in one place the Ari's most prominent disciple, Rabbi Hayyim Vital, indicates that the Radbaz was the Ari's master.
9. Some authorities, such as Maimonides in his *Guide to the Perplexed* and the *Sefer ha-Ikkarim,* give a different interpretation of this midrash, but it is certainly more easily understood in light of the principle put forth by *Sefer ha-Temunah.*
10. *Sefer ha-Temunah* 314.
11. Here again it is important to note that the Ari presents an entirely different interpretation of the teaching that "God created universes and destroyed them," saying that it refers to spiritual rather than physical universes. This is in line with the Ari's general opposition to the concept of Sabbatical cycles before the creation. Many of the major early Kabbalists opposed the Ari in this respect.
12. Hagigah 13b.
13. Bahya, Ziyyoni, and Recanati on Leviticus 25:8.
14. See *Kuzari* 1:67, Ramban on Genesis 2:3, Ibn Ezra on Genesis 8:22.
15. The complete text of Rabbi Lipschitz's *Derush* will be found below in the appendix to this volume.
16. *Derush Or ha-Hayyim* 4a (see below, pp. 108-116).
17. The only complete manuscript is in the Lenin State Library, Moscow (Guenzburg Collection, no. 775).
18. *Ozar ha-Hayyim,* p. 86b. See the appendix to this article for the full text.
19. Eruvin 18a, Berakhot 61a.
20. Rosh Hashanah 11b-12a.
21. Tosafot to Rosh Hashanah 27a, s.v. *ke-ma'an.* See also *Or ha-Hayyim* on Genesis 1:1, no. 16.
22. *Peri Ez Hayyim* on Rosh Hashanah service.
23. See *No'am Elimelekh, Hayyei Sarah.*
24. See *No'am Elimelekh, Bo.*
25. *Bereshit Rabbah* 12.2.

Chapter 2
Longevity and Immortality
in Judaic Sources

With rapid progress being made in discovering the causes of aging and death, science today stands on the threshold of eliminating these frailties, which hitherto have been considered inevitable parts of the human life-cycle. At the same time, discussion of the ethical and theological problems raised by the prospects of extreme longevity has become all the more important. If science succeeds in extending human life and eliminating death, questions will arise regarding the desirability and moral consequences of such steps.

In classical Jewish teaching, there is considerable discussion about the reasons for aging and death, as well as the possibility of their elimination.

According to the Torah, man was originally created as an immortal creature.[1] God thus commanded Adam not to eat from the Tree of Knowledge, saying, "On the day that you eat from it, you will surely die" (Genesis 2:17). This did not mean that Adam would die immediately, since the Torah clearly states that Adam subsequently lived for 930 years. The meaning was that a process would be initiated through which death would eventually overtake him.[2] In modern terms, this means that a biological clock was set, through which the body would ultimately terminate its own life processes.

Still, as the Torah relates, the generations following Adam enjoyed what would now be considered extreme longevity (for the exact figures, see the table). Of the generations between

17

Adam and Noah, the greatest age was attained by Methuselah, who lived to be 969 years old. The average age at death for these ten generations was 857.5 years, and if the anomalously short lives of Enoch and Lamech are not counted, the average was 929 years.

LONGEVITY OF EARLY BIBLICAL GENERATIONS

Name	Age at fatherhood	Age at death	Ratio
Adam	130	930	7.15
Seth	105	912	8.69
Enosh	90	905	10.06
Kenan	70	910	13.0
Mahalalel	65	895	13.77
Jared	162	962	5.94
Enoch	65	365	5.62
Methuselah	187	969	5.18
Lamech	182	777	4.27
Noah (Great Flood)	500	950	1.9
Shem	100	600	6.0
Arpachshad	35	438	13.69
Shelah	30	433	14.43
Eber	34	464	13.65
Peleg (Tower of Babel)	30	239	7.97
Reu	32	239	7.47
Serug	30	230	7.67
Nahor	29	148	5.10
Terah	70	205	2.93

Also important are the ages when these individuals fathered children. Noah was the oldest, becoming a father at 500, while the youngest were Mahalalel and Enoch, both of whom fathered their first child at the age of 65. The average age of paternity was 117 years.[3]

The classical Jewish commentators took these figures very seriously. The possibility that the years mentioned in the Torah may have been shorter than the present calendar year is discussed in the major commentaries but is universally discounted.[4] There are exegetical reasons for this.

First, the Torah states that Mahalalel was 65 years old when he fathered Jared. If we assume that the Biblical year was only a fifth of an actual year, then Mahalalel would have been 13 at the time. But on the same scale, Methuselah would still have lived to be 194 years old, and the average age at death would have been 186.

To adjust the length of the Biblical year so that the average age at death would be 120, a high but possible figure, we would have to say that an actual year is equivalent to 7.74 Biblical years. On the same scale, however, we would then have to assume that Mahalalel was slightly over eight years old when he fathered a child. It is therefore obvious that it is impossible to reconcile the figures by adjusting the length of the Biblical year.

Furthermore, from the account of the Great Flood, it is obvious that the year mentioned in the Torah is a normal year consisting of twelve normal months.[5] Yet, following this account, the Torah clearly states that Noah lived for 950 of these years. However one may interpret its significance, it is clear that the Torah literally states that these generations lived to be over 900 years old.

The earliest known commentator to offer an interpretation of this pattern of longevity was Josephus, a Jewish historian who flourished in the first century.[6] He offers several reasons for the long lives these individuals enjoyed. First, they were close to the initial creation of man and were "beloved by God." Moreover, their diet contributed to their longevity, which indicates that even unusually long lifespans are within the realm of physical possibility. Finally, they were granted long life so that they would be able to make long-term astronomical observations and thus discover the laws of astronomy, a view that is shared by the Midrash.[7] Josephus also cites numerous early Greek and Egyptian historians who speak of people having lived close to a thousand years.[8]

According to Maimonides, the longevity mentioned in the Torah was very rare, confined to those people actually named in the text.[9] Like Josephus, he attributes their longevity to diet, as well as to their general lifestyle, indicating that such long life is not beyond the realm of normal human potential. Nevertheless, Maimonides does not discount the possibility that the extreme longevity of these early generations might have been miraculous. The same view is apparently also held by Gersonides (Ralbag).[10]

Maimonides' general thesis that only the individuals actually named in the text enjoyed such extreme lifespans is strongly disputed by Nahmanides (Ramban).[11] He indicates that all of Adam's early descendants lived extraordinarily long lives, primarily because of their biological perfection. According to his opinion, the reduction of the human lifespan was a result of the climatic changes resulting from the Great Flood in the generation of Noah.

Another major commentator, Isaac Abarbanel, saw this longevity as a result of temperance in diet and sexual activity.[12] He notes that most members of the early generations did not father children until their seventh decade, a very advanced age by present standards. According to this opinion, the same differences in the biological clock that resulted in extreme longevity may also have delayed adolescence until the sixth decade or later. The hormonal differences may also have resulted in a much weaker sexual drive.

At this point it is important to note that according to many classical Jewish sources, Adam was not the first human being to be created. According to this school, there were numerous previous acts of creation, and the one described in the Torah is merely the most recent. The Talmud thus speaks of 974 generations that existed before Adam.[13] In the same vein, the Midrash states that before this creation "God created worlds and destroyed them."[14] As these teachings are interpreted by a number of sources, especially among the Kabbalists, they refer to earlier cycles of creation. Adam was merely the first human being created in the latest cycle.[15]

According to these opinions, it would seem that man already had the physical and mental capacities that we possess as early as 974 generations before Adam, or some twenty-five thousand years ago. According to Jewish teachings, Adam himself was created in 3761 B.C.E., and this date can actually be calculated from the Biblical account.[16]

Thus, even though pre-Adamic man had a "normal" lifespan, Adam was created without his biological clock being set for eventual death. When he ate from the Tree of Knowledge, however, the biological clock was set to terminate his life, but Adam still enjoyed extraordinary longevity, and this trait was inherited by his descendants.

In order to preserve this trait, the descendants of Adam apparently inbred among themselves.[17] It also appears that Adam and his descendants lived a secluded existence, separated from the rest of humanity. That is why Cain was fearful about venturing into the outside world, saying, "All who find me will kill me" (Genesis 4:14).[18]

Viewing the longevity mentioned in the Torah as a hereditary trait confined to Adam's descendants also explains how it was gradually reduced. The Torah cryptically states, "The sons of God saw the daughters of man that they were fair, and they took for themselves wives from all whom they chose" (Genesis 6:2). According to the Midrash, the "children of God" were the descendants of Adam, who enjoyed extreme longevity.[19] Thus, the descendants of Adam began to intermarry with the surrounding primitive human stock, and this interbreeding resulted in a reduction in the group's average lifespan. The account therefore continues that God declared, "My spirit shall not abide in man forever, for he is mere flesh, but his days shall be 120 years" (Genesis 6:3). According to many sources, this meant that as a result of inbreeding, 120 years would ultimately become the practical limit to man's lifespan.[20] Others, however, say it meant that mankind as a whole would only live another 120 years and then the Flood would occur. According to this opinion, the verse was a warning, given 120 years before the Flood.[21]

After the Flood, inbreeding between the children of Noah stabilized the strain of longevity, resulting in a lifespan about half that of Adam. The descendants of Noah then migrated to the east, eventually to Babylon (Iraq), where they interbred with other tribes.[22] The longevity trait was thus diluted again, and in later generations we find lifetimes approximately one-fourth those of the earliest generations. Thus, if the average earliest lifespan was 929 years, that, in the generations following the Flood, was 445 years, while in later generations, following the building of the Tower of Babel, it was 228 years.

***

According to Jewish sources, one of the important charac-teristics of the Messianic Age is that the longevity enjoyed by the earliest generations will be shared by the entire human race. The most important prophecy regarding this is found in the Book of Isaiah. The prophet states, "From then on, there will no more be one tender in years or aged, who will not fill his days, for as an adolescent (na'ar) one shall die at a hundred years old, and a sinner a hundred years old shall be [considered] cursed" (Isaiah 65:20). The classical Jewish commentators explain that this means that a person who dies at the age of a hundred will be considered to have died as an adolescent.[23]

In conventional Biblical usage, the Hebrew word na'ar used in this verse refers to a person just around puberty, usually around the age of thirteen.[24] If the verse from Isaiah is taken to indicate a slowing of the biological clock, where puberty, nor-mally taking place at age thirteen, occurs at age one hundred, then the lifespan can be expected to be increased by a factor of 7.7. The outer limit of the human lifespan, which is currently around 120, would then be 923 years, very close to the average age of the first generations after Adam. Thus, most commentaries on this verse note that the longevity indicated by this prophecy means that the lifespans existing in the pre-Noachide generations will be restored. A similar idea—that what Adam lost will be restored in Messianic times—is also found in the Midrash.[25]

At this point it is important to emphasize that, according to many important Jewish thinkers, the Messianic Age will not be a time of miracles, and no laws of nature will be changed.[26] This is particularly true in the teachings of Maimonides, who states that prophecies that appear to predict miracles actually refer to technological rather than literal miracles.[27]

Another important point stressed in the writings of Maimonides is that the Messianic Age will be a time when war and strife are eliminated and human potential is realized to its fullest degree. The Messiah himself is not seen as a superhuman being, but as an inspired leader who will bring all this about.

It is therefore particularly significant that Maimonides clearly states that in the Messianic Age people will enjoy extremely long lives because of their carefree existence.[28] Since Maimonides consistently maintains that no laws of nature will be violated in the Messianic Age, one possibility is that there will be scientific or technological progress, though he makes no mention of this.

In another verse in the same prophecy discussed earlier, Isaiah repeats this theme: "They will not build for others to dwell, they will not plant for others to eat; for as the days of a tree shall be the days of My people, and My chosen ones will outlive the work of their hands" (Isaiah 65:22). According to the classical commentaries, this means that man will enjoy the same longevity as a tree, enduring for many centuries.[29]

The implications of such longevity are also outlined in this prophecy, since it concludes, "The wolf and the lamb shall feed together, the lion shall eat straw like the ox, and dust shall be the serpent's food—they shall not hurt nor destroy on all My holy mountain, says God" (Isaiah 65:25).[30] According to many commentators, including Maimonides, the statement that animals will live in peace is an allegory relating to universal peace in nature, especially among the human race.[31] This prophecy would thus be very closely related to the one that states, "They will beat their swords into plowshares, their spears into pruning hooks; nation will not lift up sword against nation, neither will they learn war anymore" (Isaiah 2:4).

Man's aggressiveness toward his fellows is closely related to his awareness of imminent mortality. A person who can look forward to several centuries of fruitful life, on the other hand, would be much less willing to risk his life in war. As a result, the realization of extreme longevity can result in the abolishment of war and universal peace, both internal and external. With the wealth of nations diverted from war, more resources will be available to improve the lot of humanity as a whole. The Messianic Age will thus be a time when the full human potential is realized, without the self-destructiveness resulting from aggression.

According to classical Jewish interpretations, there is also a prophecy that death will eventually be abolished completely: "He will swallow up death forever, and the Lord God will wipe away tears from all faces" (Isaiah 25:8).[32] There is one opinion in the Talmud that the majority of humanity will enjoy extremely long lives, but for a small minority, death will be abolished completely.[33] Others, however, maintain that death will eventually be abolished for all mankind.[34]

* * *

In general, the fact that man is mortal is viewed as having some positive aspects. The Talmud states that King Hezekiah's concealing of the "Book of Remedies" was a virtuous act. As Rashi explains, people should be reminded of their mortality and pray for mercy.[35] If man were immortal, it would be very easy for him to become totally immersed in the material world and forget life's spiritual values.[36] Immortality and extreme longevity will therefore have to wait until the Messianic Age, when spiritual values will be firmly imbedded in man's nature.

Death is not without its positive value, as the Talmud notes. When an older generation dies, it gives the younger a chance for accomplishment. Resh Lakish is thus quoted as saying, "Let us show gratitude to our ancestors, since if they had not sinned, we would not have come into the world."[37] If earlier generations had not sinned, they would have been immortal. According to the Talmud's conclusion, Resh Lakish is implying that without the leveling effect of death, the people of later generations would never attain any position of influence, since they would never be able to compete with people from earlier generations. One reason is that the members of the earlier generations would establish themselves in positions of power from which they could not be budged. Even without this, however, younger people would find it difficult to compete against the superior experience of individuals who had already lived for centuries.

Nonetheless, in almost the same breath, the Talmud says, "If there were no death, nothing would be better than that." Even though immortality might bring some disadvantages, they are vastly overwhelmed by the advantages.

This may to some extent be linked with the prophecy of Isaiah, discussed earlier, which ties longevity to a diminution of aggressiveness and competition. In a noncompetitive world, the advantages of position and experience would not overwhelm the younger generation, since all concern would be for the mutual good. In such a world, each individual would be allowed to attain his greatest possible potential, and the existence of people with greater wisdom and experience would be an advantage rather than a disadvantage. The experience of age would be combined with the imagination and inventiveness of youth to create the best of possible worlds.

NOTES

1. Avodah Zarah 5a, *Bereshit Rabbah* 16:6. There is an opinion, however, that the Angel of Death was formed on the first day of creation, even before Adam sinned; see *Tanhuma Vayeshev* 4; Ramban and Bahya on Genesis 2:17. Also see commentaries on Genesis 3:22.

2. See Ramban on Genesis 2:17; Rabbi Moses Hayyim Luzzatto, *Derekh ha-Shem* 1:3:9.

3. For details, see Genesis 5. Regarding the generations after the Flood, see Genesis 11:12-32.

4. See Abarbanel on Genesis 5.

5. See Genesis 7:11, 8:4-6, 13, 14; *Seder Olam* 4; Rashi on Genesis 8:5. Also see commentaries on Genesis 8:22. Regarding the life of Noah, see Genesis 9:29.

6. *Antiquities* 1:3:9.

7. *Bereshit Rabbah* 26:5. Also see *Bereshit Rabbah* 10:4, Abarbanel on Genesis 5.

8. Josephus mentions Manetho, Berosus, Mochus, Hesitaeus, Hieronymus, Hesiod, Hecataeus, Hellanicus, Acusilaus, Ephorus, and Nicolaus.

9. *Moreh Nevukhim* 2:47.

10. Commentary on Genesis 5. Also see *Kuzari* 1:95 (59b).

11. Commentary on Genesis 5:4. Cf. Radak on Isaiah 65:20.

12. Commentary on Genesis 5. Cf. Shabbat 152a.

13. Hagigah 13b-14a; *Kohelet Rabbah* 1:15, 4:3; *Tanhuma Lekh Lekha* 11, *Yitro* 9; *Midrash Tehillim* 105:3; *Yalkut Shimoni* 2:863.

14. *Bereshit Rabbah* 3:7, 9:2; *Kohelet Rabbah* 3:11. Also see *Bereshit Rabbah* 10:2.

15. See Chapter 1, and *Sefer ha-Temunah*, gimel, dalet; *Ma'arekhet Elokut* 13 (190a); *Sefer ha-Kaneh* (Cracow, 5654), 78b and other places; *Teshuvot Rashba* 1:423; Rabbi Moses Cordovero, *Shi'ur Komah* 83; Rabbi David ibn Zimra, *Magen David*, gimel, dalet; *Mezudat David* 298; Rabbi Isaac of Akko, *Ozar ha-Hayyim* (Guenzburg MS 775), p. 86b; *Sha'arei Gan Eden, Orah Zaddikim* 1:1. Cf. Bahya, Recanati, and Ziyyoni on Leviticus 25:8; *Sefer ha-Hinnukh* 330; Ibn Ezra on Genesis 1:5, 8:22. For a philosophical discussion, see *Derush Or ha-Hayyim* 3 (in appendix to this volume).

16. See the following on the exact time of Adam's creation: Rosh Hashanah 10b; Yerushalmi Avodah Zarah 1:2 (3a); *Vayikra Rabbah* 29:1; Tosafot to Rosh Hashanah 8a, s.v. *le-tekufot*; R. Nissan to Rosh Hashanah (Rif 3a), s.v. *be-rosh*; Tosafot Yom Tov to Rosh Hashanah 1:2, s.v. *be-rosh*.

17. Accordingly, tradition teaches that Cain married his twin sister: *Pirkei de-Rabbi Eliezer* 21 (48a-b); Rashi on Leviticus 20:17, based on Yevamot 62a and Sanhedrin 38b; see Tosafot to Sanhedrin 38b, s.v. *va-yardu*; *Bereshit Rabbah* 22:3.

18. Most commentators, however, state that Cain feared that the animals would kill him; see Rashi on Genesis 4:15, *Bereshit Rabbah* 22:12.

19. *Bereshit Rabbah* 26:5, Abarbanel on Genesis 5:6, Ramban on Genesis 6:4.

20. *Midrash ha-Gadol* on Genesis 6:3; see Hulin 137b.

21. *Seder Olam* 28; Rashi and Ibn Ezra on Genesis 6:3.

22. See Genesis 11:2 (see Rosh), 10:25.

23. Ibn Ezra and Radak, ad loc.

24. At the age of one hundred, one will thus be considered like a thirteen-year-old; *Bereshit Rabbah* 26:2.

25. *Bereshit Rabbah* 12:6, *Bemidbar Rabbah* 13:12.

26. Sanhedrin 99a, Shabbat 63a.

27. Commentary on Sanhedrin 10:1. Cf. Melakhim 11:3.

28. Commentary on Sanhedrin 10:1; *Iggeret Tehiyat ha-Metim* (Warsaw, 1927), p. 11.

29. Ibn Ezra ad loc., and see above, n. 25.

30. See also Isaiah 11:6-9.

31. See *Yad, Melakhim* 12:1.

32. See Abarbanel ad loc.; Mo'ed Katan 3:9 (28b); Bertinoro ad loc.; *Mekhilta* to Exodus 12:25; *Shemot Rabbah* 15:21; *Kohelet Rabbah* 1:4; *Tanhuma Yitro* 17, *Emor* 3; Tosafot to Rosh Hashanah 16b, s.v. *kedei*. Some say, however, that this only speaks of accidental death and not that resulting from old age; see Radak ad loc., *Devarim Rabbah* 2:30.

33. Pesahim 68a, Sanhedrin 91b. Rashi ad loc. writes that this refers to the period following the resurrection, but *Yad Ramah*, ibid., states that it is before the resurrection.

34. Both opinions are found in *Bereshit Rabbah* 26:2.

35. Berakhot 10b and Pesahim 56a. One who is sick should imagine himself as one being led to execution and thus repent, Shabbat 32a.

36. Avot 2:10, Shabbat 153a, *Midrash Tehillim* 90:16. See also *Bereshit Rabbah* 9:5, where the need to keep man's overweening ego in place is stressed; Bava Batra 75a.

37. Rashi on Avodah Zarah 5a, s.v. *ke-mi*. Cf. *Avodat ha-Kodesh* 2:21 (41d).

Chapter 3
On the Resurrection

One of our fundamental beliefs is the belief in the resurrection of the dead. We believe that there will come a time when all the dead will be brought back to life, and body and soul will be reunited. Thus, the last of the Thirteen Principles of Faith reads, "I believe with perfect faith that there will be a resurrection of the dead at a time which will please the Creator."

The resurrection is alluded to in the Torah when God says, "I kill and bring back to life" (Deuteronomy 32:39).[1] This belief is expressed more explicitly in the words of the prophet, "Your dead shall live, dead bodies shall arise; awake and sing, you who dwell in the dust" (Isaiah 26:19). The concept is expressed most clearly in the Book of Daniel: "Many who sleep in the dust shall awake, some to everlasting life, and some to reproach and everlasting abhorrence" (12:2).

There are, however, two basic opinions regarding the resurrection.

The majority opinion, held by Saadiah Gaon,[2] the Ra'avad,[3] the Ramban (Nahmanides),[4] and all the Kabbalists,[5] is that the resurrection is the first step leading to the world-to-come.[6] According to this opinion, the resurrected dead will live on forever, and the world-to-come will exist on a physical plane where body and soul are reunited.

To some extent, the rationale for this is provided in the following Talmudic passage:

Antoninus once said to Rabbi [Judah the Prince]: The body and soul can both escape God's judgment. The body can defend itself by saying, "It is the soul who sinned. For look, since the day the soul left me, I have lain still like a dumb stone [and not done any wrong]." The soul can [similarly] say, "It is the body who sinned. Since I left the body, I have flown free like a bird."

Rabbi replied: I will give you an example. A human king once had a beautiful garden, full of early figs. He set two guards over it, one crippled and one blind. The crippled guard said to the blind one, "I see beautiful fruit in this garden. Carry me on your shoulders and we will share it." They carried out this plan, the blind guard carrying the crippled one, until they had eaten all the choicest fruits in the garden.

When the king returned, he asked his two watchmen, "Where are my choicest fruits?"

The crippled guard replied, "Do I have feet [that I could go after the fruit]?" The blind one [similarly] said, "Do I have eyes to see [the fruit]?"

The king, however, was not fooled. He placed the crippled man on the blind one's shoulders, and judged them both together.

In a similar manner, God will bring the soul and return it to the body, and then judge the two together. It is thus written, "He will call to the heaven above, and to the earth below, to judge His people" [Psalms 50:4].

"He will call to the heaven above"—this is the soul.

"And to the earth below"—this is the body. [The reason why these are both called is so that God can "judge His people."[7]

The Talmud thus provides a profound reason for the resurrection. At the end of time, man will be judged as a complete person, a full human being with both body and soul. A disembodied soul may be capable of a lofty perception of the Divine, but it is not a full human being. Any judgment or reward given to such a soul could never be complete.

Many people find this difficult to understand. Since man's reward is ultimately spiritual, what need will there be for a material body? Why should the world-to-come have a material dimension?

In order to understand this, we must introduce a related question: Why did God create the physical world at all?

This is not so trivial a question as it may seem. God Himself is certainly spiritual, and so is the good that He offers to His world. It is obvious that the purpose of creation is essentially spiritual. If so, then why did God create the physical world?

This point is discussed at length in our classical literature.[8] In order to answer it, however, we must first introduce still another question: What precisely is the difference between the spiritual and the material?

The answer is really quite simple. The main difference between the spiritual and the physical involves the concept of space. Physical space exists only in the physical world. In the spiritual domain, there is no concept of space as we know it.[9]

But still, we speak of being far apart or close in the spiritual world. Our sages teach us that spiritual closeness involves resemblance. Two things that resemble each other are spiritually close, while two that differ are far apart.[10]

This has very important implications. In the spiritual world it is impossible to bring opposites together. Because they are opposites, they are, by definition, poles apart.

Spiritual things, however, may still be bound to the material, much as the soul is bound to the body. If two spiritual opposites are bound to the same material object, they can be brought together, for in the physical world we can literally push two opposites together.[11]

Thus, for example, man has both an urge for good and an urge for evil, the *yezer ha-tov* and the *yezer ha-ra*. In a purely spiritual sense, the two are poles apart, and without the material could never be brought together in a single entity. Angels, for instance, have no evil urge.[12] It is only in a physical body that good and evil can be brought together. Although they are at opposite poles spiritually, they come together in the physical man.[13]

God and man are also worlds apart—"as the heavens are higher than the earth."[14] This is even true of man's soul. On a purely spiritual plane, it would be totally impossible for the two ever to be brought together. All the meditating and philosophizing in the world would be unable to bridge this gap.

It is only here in the physical world that God and man can come together. This is why God created the concept of mitzvot, or commandments. The physical act involved in a mitzvah is intimately bound to God's will, for it is His will that we do a particular physical act. In observing a mitzvah we are literally binding ourselves to God,[15] as is shown by the fact that the word's root means "to bind."[16] Every mitzvah serves to bind us to God.

This, however, can only take place on the physical plane. It is only when both God and man are bound to the same physical act that they can be bound together. On the spiritual plane, there is no way for this to occur.

It was for this reason, essentially, that God created a physical world.

With this background in view, we are able to understand an essential difference between man, who consists of both the material and the spiritual, and the angels, who are purely spiritual. Since an angel cannot bind itself to God through any physical act, it cannot elevate itself. Only man can do so, since he is bound to a physical body. Thus, when God showed the prophet a vision of angels, He told him, "I will give you a place among those standing here" (Zechariah 3:7). The angels among whom he moves are "standing" and unchanging,[17] while man is capable of physical movement and spiritual progress.

But just as man is not meant to rest on his laurels in this world, neither should he do so in the future world. Our sages teach us, "The righteous have no rest, neither in this world nor in the next. It is thus written, 'They go from strength to strength [all who stand before God]' (Psalm 84:8)."[18]

This explains why the body has a role to play in the future world.

According to those who hold this opinion, then, the resurrection is a permanent state, leading directly to the world-to-come. The Talmudic teaching that the resurrected dead will never return to the dust seems to support this view.[19]

As was mentioned earlier, however, there is another opinion on the resurrection, that of the Rambam (Maimonides),[20]

Rabbi Judah Halevi,[21] and several other early writers.[22] According to this opinion, the world-to-come is purely spiritual, and the resurrection is only a transient state. Some say that the dead will be brought back to life in order to partake of the Messianic Age,[23] others that they will be revivified in order to show God's dominance over all things, even life and death.[24]

The world-to-come is thus identical to the "world of souls" that a human soul enters immediately after death. According to Maimonides and those who follow his views, the body experiences death twice. First comes "natural" death, eventually to be followed by the resurrection. After this the body dies again and returns to a purely spiritual future world.

This second opinion finds support in the following passage from the *Midrash Tanhuma*:

> This is why our sages call this [future life] the world-to-come, not because it does not exist now, but because from our point of view it is "to come." It is the "world-to-come" because it follows after man's life in this world. As for those who say that this world will be destroyed and then the world-to-come will begin, this is not the case. When the righteous depart this world, they immediately [enter the world-to-come].[25]

Recapitulating, there are two major opinions regarding the resurrection and the world-to-come.

1. Immediately after death, man's soul enters the world of souls (*olam ha-neshamot*) to await the resurrection. In the resurrected state, with body and soul rejoined, he partakes of the world-to-come.

2. The world of souls *is* the world-to-come, and is a permanent state. It is temporarily interrupted for the resurrection, but the resurrected death will die again and return to the purely spiritual world-to-come.

These two opinions may have existed even in Talmudic times. Quoting the disciples of Rabbi Ishmael, the Midrash brings the opinion cited earlier that body and soul will be judged together, citing the parable of the two watchmen, and then brings another opinion, that of Rabbi Hiyya.

> In the future world, God will overlook the body and only judge the soul. The soul will complain, "Master of the world, both of us have sinned together. Why do You leave the body and single me out for judgment?"
>
> God will then reply, "The body comes from below, a place of sin. But you come from on high, a place where sin does not exist. Therefore, you alone are worthy of being judged."[26]

According to the Midrash, it would appear that the disciples of Rabbi Ishmael followed the first opinion, while Rabbi Hiyya followed the second. This would explain why we find Midrashim that support both opinions.

If the ultimate purpose of the resurrection causes some confusion, its mode causes even more, since it involves a miracle of the highest order.

The earliest picture of the resurrection comes from the prophecy of Ezekiel, where a most vivid picture is painted.

> The hand of God was set upon me, and He carried me away with His spirit and put me in a valley full of bones. He made me walk up and down among them. There were very many bones in the open valley, and they were very dry.
>
> God then said to me, "Son of man, can these bones live again?" I answered, "Only You know, O God."
>
> He said to me, "Prophesy over these bones, and say to them: Dry bones, hear God's word."
>
> This was God's word to these bones: "I will put a spirit in you, and you will live. I will put sinews on you, make flesh grow over you, cover you with skin, and give you breath. Then you shall live, and know that I am God."
>
> I began to prophesy as God told me. As I prophesied, there was a noise, a sound of clattering, and the bones joined together. And as I looked, sinews appeared on them, flesh grew over them, and skin covered them. But still, there was no life in them.
>
> God then said to me, "Prophesy to the spirit son of man, and say to it: 'Come, spirit, from every direction, and enter these corpses', so that they may come to life."

I began prophesying as God had told me, and a spirit entered them. They came back to life and stood on their feet, a great, immense army.

Then God said to me, "Son of man, these bones are the people of Israel. They say, 'Our bones are dry, our hope is gone, the final decree has been set against us.'

"Therefore, prophesy, and say to them, 'This is the word of God: I will open your graves, My people, and bring you up from them, and return you to the land of Israel. You shall know that I am God, when I open your graves, raise you up from them, and let you live in your own land. You shall then know that I am God, and I will do as I have spoken.' This is God's word."

This amazing account in the thirty-seventh chapter of the Book of Ezekiel gives us a vivid picture of the resurrection. Nevertheless, in the Talmud we find a dispute as to whether this incident actually happened, or whether it was merely a vision.[27] From the context, we see that this issue is related to the question of whether or not we can learn anything about the final resurrection from Ezekiel. The Talmud states that according to the opinion that it was a mere vision, we cannot.

The question is discussed in more detail in a Midrash.

The School of Shammai says: Man will not be formed in the future world as he is in this world. In this world, his formation begins with skin and flesh, with bones and sinews growing later. In the future world, on the other hand, it will begin with bones and sinews, and skin and flesh will grow upon them. We thus find [the following in connection with] the dead of Ezekiel, "And as I looked, sinews appeared on them, flesh grew over them, and skin covered them" (Ezekiel 37:8). Said R. Yonatan: We do not take the dead of Ezekiel as an example. To what can they be compared? To a man who enters a bathhouse. What he takes off last, he puts on first.

The School of Hillel says: Man will be formed in the future world just as he is in this one. In both cases his formation will begin with skin and flesh, and end with sinews and bones. Thus it is written, "You will pour me out like milk and curdle me like cheese. You will then clothe me with skin and flesh, and knit me together with bones and sinews" (Job 10:10-11). [This is written in

> the future tense and refers to the resurrection. It can be compared to a dish of milk.] Until rennet is added, it is completely liquid. But once rennet is added, it curdles and becomes solid. Thus Job said, "You will pour me out like milk and curdle me like cheese.... You will grant me life and favor, and Your providence will restore my spirit."[28]

We find a very important difference of opinion here. The School of Shammai likens the final resurrection to that of Ezekiel's prophecy, where flesh and skin will miraculously cover the bones of the dead. The dead will then rise, just like those resurrected by Ezekiel.

The School of Hillel takes a completely different position. In their view, the resurrection will parallel the birth process. The new body will begin as an embryo, with "skin and flesh," but no bones or sinews. Like an embryo, it will gradually grow and develop to form the resurrected body. The process may still be miraculous, but it is certainly not on the same grand scale as what is envisioned by the first opinion.

There is another element in the resurrection tradition, and that is the *luz*, the physical part from which the body will eventually be resurrected. The *luz* is mentioned several times in the Midrash; one good example is the following: "Hadrian asked Rabbi Joshua ben Korha, 'From what will God resurrect man in the future world?' Rabbi Joshua replied, 'From the *luz* on the spine.' "[29] Rabbi Joshua went on to demonstrate that the *luz* was indestructible. In another Midrash, the existence of the *luz* is found to be alluded to in the verse, "The almond shall blossom" (Ecclesiastes 12:5).[30]

The identity of the *luz* is not absolutely certain. Some commentators speak of it as the coccyx, the lowest bone of the spine.[31] There are others, however, including the Kabbalists,[32] who identify it with the "scoop of dust," or *tarvad shel rakav*, that comprises the final decay product of the body.[33] This opinion is substantiated by a Midrash.

> Rabbi Simeon said: All bodies remain in the earth until all that remains of them is a scoop of dust (*tarvad shel rakav*). This

> becomes mixed with the dust of the earth, just like yeast put in dough. In the future world, when God calls the earth to bring forth all bodies, this dust will germinate in the earth, just like yeast in dough. It will then grow and bring forth the body without blemish.[34]

It appears here that Rabbi Simeon follows the opinion of the School of Hillel, and we will presently see that this is indeed true. What he is saying is that the final decay products of the body can be made to grow into a new resurrected body. The process is likened to yeast germinating and growing in a mass of dough.

There is a third element in the tradition, the "dew of resurrection." It is mentioned in several passages,[35] particularly in the Yerushalmi, which states: "The resurrection will come about through dew. Thus it is written, 'Your dead shall live, dead bodies shall arise ... for your dew is the dew of light' (Isaiah 26:19)."[36]

From this tradition, we see that the process of growth will be stimulated or initiated by the dew of resurrection. This is also discussed in the Zohar.

> Rabbi Hiyya said: It is man's original body that will arise. Thus it is written, "Your dead shall live"—they will live again and not be recreated.
>
> For one bone remains in the earth and never rots or disappears. When the time comes, God will soften it, and make it germinate like yeast in dough. It will grow and spread in all four directions, and from it the body and all its limbs will be reconstructed. After that, God Himself will give it a spirit of life.
>
> Rabbi Eleazer added: This bone will be dissolved in the dew of resurrection. Thus it is written, "For your dew is the dew of light."[37]

Here we have a clear indication that man's final remains will be dissolved in the dew of resurrection and will thus be stimulated to grow into a new body. Another important point that we see here is that God will provide the new body with a soul only *after* it is reconstructed. This would seem to indicate that the body itself might be reconstructed by man, and indeed there is a tradition that the resurrection will take place through the righteous.[38]

An even clearer picture of the resurrection is provided by another passage in the Zohar. Here we find Rabbi Phinehas quoting the opinion of the School of Shammai that the resurrection will parallel that of Ezekiel. Rabbi Simeon replies:

> This was already disputed in earlier generations. But God will perform miracles and unusual wonders with these bones. It is thus written, "Remember that You fashioned me like clay, and will bring me into dust again" (Job 10:9). After that, Scripture states, "You will pour me out like milk and curdle me like cheese. You will clothe me with skin and flesh, and knit me together with bones and sinews" (Job 10:10).
>
> After man decays in the ground, and the time of the resurrection comes, God will take the bones that remain and process them like dough, just as cheese is made from milk. The process will be like the fermentation of milk, which is a very purified fermentation.
>
> The bone will be separated into very small pieces and ground until it is a liquid like milk. It will then be curdled and given a form, just as cheese is curdled out of milk. It will then be formed into skin, flesh, sinew, and bone. Thus it is written, "You will pour me out like milk."[39]

The remains regenerate: first they will have to be liquified or dissolved until they form a liquid like milk. This will have to take place under very "pure," or sterile, conditions. The resulting liquid will then "curdle" into an embryo, which will in turn grow to form the new body.

As we shall see, we already find ourselves discussing a process that verges on scientific possibility. Before we go into this in detail, however, let us look into the question of just how miraculous the resurrection is meant to be.

In defending his view that the resurrection is only temporary, and that the resurrected dead will live but a short while and then die again, the Rambam states that many sources in our sacred literature prove that a miracle can only produce a temporary result.[40] This appears to be an unbroken rule—no miracle can result in anything permanent. Nature follows its normal course, and a miracle can only temporarily abrogate it. An interesting consequence of this may be that no permanent record is left of miracles, and therefore we should not expect to find any archaeological evidence for them.

The Rambam argues that since the resurrection is patently a miracle, its effects can only be temporary. This is one of his strongest proofs that the resurrected dead will eventually have to die.

However, as we have seen, there is still a majority opinion that the resurrected dead will live forever. According to this opinion, the Rambam's objection remains a glaring question. This objection remains unanswered unless we say that the resurrection does not involve the alteration of any of the laws of nature.

Whether the resurrected dead will live forever or not may be related to the dispute between the School of Shammai and the School of Hillel. Shammai derives the details of the resurrection from Ezekiel's vision, where the dead were revived miraculously and eventually died. Hillel's School, on the other hand, derives the details from embryonic development, which does not involve any manifest miracle. It is logical to assume that the Hillelites hold that the resurrected dead can live forever. Indeed, in the Talmud, we find that those who maintain that the resurrected dead will live forever also hold that the story in Ezekiel was only a vision and cannot be applied to the final resurrection.

Now, although we must qualify our remarks as conjectural, the lessons that we can learn from this are quite remarkable.

Instead of viewing this matter from a traditional viewpoint, let us for a moment explore the possibility of bringing a dead person back to life as a purely technological problem. The newly developed science of cloning comes into play here. As is well known, almost every cell in the body contains a full set of chromosomes, with all the genetic material needed to reconstruct the entire body. In the standard method of cloning, which has already been successfully tried with animals, the chromosomes of an unfertilized ovum are replaced with those of the cell to be cloned. If this ovum is then implanted in a womb, it will grow into a precise genetic carbon copy of the chromosome donor.

What if an amount of genetic material sufficient to reproduce a full set of chromosomes were to survive in a grave? Cloning could then be done not only from a living person but even from one long dead.

Furthermore, there is no reason why this process should have to take place in a natural womb. There has been much experimentation with artificial wombs, and it is certainly conceivable that a clone could be grown in an artificial womb.

Taking this one step further, the process could also be carried out with an artificial ovum, or with some other mechanism where the genetic material could first develop into a cellular structure and then into a growing embryo.

All this would be the wildest conjecture if it did not fit our traditions so very well. Thus, we speak of the dew of resurrection, which might very well be some sort of nutrient solution or, more probably, some substance that can extract and reassemble the genetic material from human remains. We find the bones being dissolved in this dew. The Zohar clearly states that this will take place under sterile conditions. The allusions to fermentation may refer to some sort of genetic viruses that may conceivably be employed in this process. The final result is the structuring of the genetic material and its development into an embryo, also clearly alluded to in the last quotation from the Zohar.

The only problem would then be to locate the remains of all the people to be resurrected. This, however, could be done prophetically. We have the precedent where Rabbi Isaac Luria, the holy Ari, located the graves of many Zaddikim through divine inspiration.[41] We furthermore find a tradition that one of the requirements for the resurrection is prophecy: "Divine inspiration (*ru'ah ha-kodesh*) brings the resurrection."[42]

Bodily resurrection may also be possible even when no remains exist. There are many cases where a body is completely destroyed and no genetic material remains. The main thing necessary to reconstruct a human body, however, is information—namely, the information contained in the genetic code.

If one had a record of the genetic code of any individual, whether recorded in a book or in any other manner, one would, in theory at least, be able to make a perfect carbon copy of this individual's body. No actual remains would be needed. All that a sufficiently advanced technology would need would be a precise record of the individual's genetic code.

Using this information, seed molecules of DNA could be produced, and these in turn could be built up into a complete set of artificial genes and chromosomes. Once these existed, the process of cloning could take place the same as with natural chromosomes.

Only one question would remain. How do we recover this information? How do we obtain the genetic code of someone who has been dead for thousands of years?

There is one obvious answer: information can be transmitted verbally. When no other method exists, the information contained in the genetic code of any individual could be revealed prophetically. This indeed may be another reason why prophecy is a necessary precondition for the resurrection.

Indeed, this may even be alluded to in the Midrash that says, "It is prophecy that will grant flesh, sinews, and bones to the dead. This is also true of all flesh and bones that have been eaten by animals and birds."[43] What this Midrash may be telling us is that when all the genetic material has been destroyed, as when a person is eaten by a wild animal, it will be restored prophetically.

The missing genetic coding could be supplied prophetically and would then be used to construct artificial chromosomes. A more fascinating possibility, however, is that the very process of prophecy could be used to reconstruct the chromosomes by a telekinetic process of some kind. Indeed, the Scripture may have been referring to just such a process when it says that Ezekiel "prophesied" over the dry bones.

In all of this discussion, we speak only of the body. Even the most perfect clone, no matter how exact a carbon copy of the body it may be, does not contain the memories of the original donor.[44]

The same is true here. All that we would be able to reconstruct technologically is the body. The memories that were in the dead person's brain are beyond the power of any technology to reproduce—this is guaranteed by the second law of thermodynamics. Thus, even if the body could be reconstructed technologically, the soul and its memories would have to be supplied by God Himself. This is also clearly stated in all our traditions.

As we noted above, this technological interpretation of the resurrection is entirely conjectural, even though it fits into our traditions very well. There are many other Talmudic and Midrashic statements that could be illuminated by this interpretation, but they were not included in this paper because of its limited scope.

In another sense, the interpretation proposed here can give us a new outlook on modern scientific developments. Without question, some of the most exciting discoveries have been made in the life sciences, especially in the fields of molecular biology and genetic engineering. As with everything new, we must ask, How does this serve God's purpose? For indeed, an important fundamental principle states that everything must ultimately serve this purpose. And if so, to what end has God given man the ability to understand the genetic code and to develop the technology to produce such things as artificial clones? If these discoveries do nothing more than provide us with insight into the resurrection, then they serve the lofty purpose of helping us to understand the Torah. If this technology should actually be used to bring about the resurrection, and ultimately the world-to-come, then we will openly see science in the service of God.

NOTES

1. Cf. Sanhedrin 91b.
2. *Emunot ve-De'ot* 7:8.
3. Ra'avad on *Yad, Teshuvah* 8:2.
4. *Torat ha-Adam,* end of *Sha'ar ha-Gemul.*
5. *Avodat ha-Kodesh* 2:42-43; *Shenei Luhot ha-Berit, Bet David* (Jerusalem, 5720), 1:31b; *Derekh ha-Shem* 1:3:9; *Derekh Mizvotekha* (*Habad*), p. 14b. Cf. Zohar 1:114a, 3:216a; *Tikkunei Zohar* 10b.
6. See Bertinoro, *Tosafot Yom Tov* on Sanhedrin 10:1; *Hiddushei ha-Ran,* ibid.
7. Sanhedrin 91a-92b. See Ritva on Rosh Hashanah 16b, s.v. *amar R. Kruspedai.*
8. See *Emunot ve-De'ot* 6:4; *Pardes Rimmonim* 31:5; *Yafeh Sha'ah* on *Ez Hayyim, Sha'ar MaN U'MaD* 4 (Tel Aviv: Ashlag, 5720), p. 192.
9. Cf. *Yad, Yesod ha-Torah* 2:5; *Pardes Rimmonim* 6:6; *Ez Hayyim, Derush Iggulim ve-Yosher* 2, ed. Ashlag, vol. 1 (5720), p. 27; *Shomer Emunim* (*ha-Kadmon*) 2:49; *Amud ha-Avodah, Hakdamah Gedolah* 15.
10. See *Amud ha-Avodah,* loc. cit.; Rabbi Yizhak Ashlag, *Hakdamah le-Sefer ha-Zohar* (in *Sulam*), 9; idem, *Talmud Eser Sefirot, Hittaklut Penimut,* pt. 1, 1:4 (p. 15).
11. See *Moreh Nevukhim,* introduction to pt. 2, no. 16; *Shefa' Tal* 1:3 (Hanau, 5372), 13c, bottom note ("Zerikhim"); *Pardes Rimmonim.* See also *Torat ha-Adam, Sha'ar ha-Gemul* (*Kitvei ha-Ramban* [Jerusalem, 5724]), p. 287.
12. Cf. Shabbat 88b-89a.
13. See Rabbi Moses Hayyim Luzzatto, *Pithei Hokhmah va-Da'at* 3.
14. Isaiah 55:9.
15. *Likkutei Amarim* (*Tanya*) 1:4; *Likkutei Maharan* 33:4, 34:4.
16. *Likkutei Maharan* 4:6. Cf. Berakhot 6b, Shabbat 30b, Rashi, s.v. *le-te'avato.*
17. *Nefesh ha-Hayyim* 1:10. Cf. *Sha'arei Kedushah* 3:2.
18. Berakhot 64a. See *Derekh Mizvotekha* 1b.
19. Sanhedrin 92a. The Rambam and those who agree with his view maintain that his opinion only follows that interpretation which takes Ezekiel's vision as mere allegory. Those who take it literally would assert that the future resurrected dead will die again, just like those of Ezekiel. This connection is indicated in the Talmudic discussion itself, and see *Iggeret Tehiyat ha-Metim* (Jerusalem, 5721), p. 11.
20. See *Yad, Teshuvah* 8:2, *Moreh Nevukhim* 2:27, *Iggeret Tehiyat ha-Metim.*
21. *Kuzari* 1:115.
22. *Hovot ha-Levavot* 4:4, *Ikkarim* 4:30, 33. *Shenei Luhot ha-Berit, Bet David* (1:16d).
23. *Or ha-Shem* (Crescas) 3:4:2.

24. *Tanhuma Vayikra* 8. Cf. *Yad, Teshuvah* 8:8.

25. Sanhedrin 91b–92a; *Vayikra Rabbah* 4:5.

26. Sanhedrin 92b.

27. *Bereshit Rabbah* 14:5. Cf. Tosafot to Niddah 25a, s.v. *or*, Rashi on Ezekiel 37:6.

28. *Bereshit Rabbah* 28:3, *Vayikra Rabbah* 18:1. Tosafot to Bava Kamma 16b, s.v. *ve-hu* (*hagehah*).

29. *Kohelet Rabbah* 12:5. *luz* is also the Talmudic word for "almond." See Bekhorot 8a.

30. *Arukh*, s.v. *luz*.

31. Cf. *Avodat ha-Kodesh* 2:40.

32. See Mishnah Nazir 7:2.

33. *Pirkei de-Rabbi Eliezer* 34. See Zohar 1:113a.

34. *Pirkei de-Rabbi Eliezer*, loc. cit.; Hagigah 12b; Zohar 1:118a, 1:130b.

35. Yerushalmi, Berakhot 5:2 (ed. Vilna, 38b), Ta'anit 1:1 (2a).

36. Zohar 2:28b, 3:222a.

37. Pesahim 68a, from Zechariah 8:4; Zohar 1:140a.

38. Zohar 2:28b, 3:222a.

39. *Iggeret Tehiyat ha-Metim*, p. 19. *Sihot ha-Ran* 141.

40. *Shemoneh Sha'arim, Sha'ar ha-Gilgulim* 36–37.

41. Avodah Zarah 20b.

42. *Pirkei de-Rabbi Eliezer* 33.

43. Thus there is an opinion that the resurrected dead will have completely new bodies. See *Ikkarim* 4:30. Also see *Avodat ha-Kodesh* 2:40.

Chapter 4
Astrology: Stars and Angels

In Jerusalem there is a Sephardic sage by the name of Hakham Shabatai.

He is a great Torah scholar who has the Talmud and codes at his fingertips. He would be a typical Jewish scholar except for one thing. Hakham Shabatai has a most unusual avocation ...

He casts horoscopes.

The Hakham will cast a horoscope for you whether he has met you or not. Just give him a birth date—and if the precise hour can be provided, the horoscope will be that much more precise. He then asks for your complete Hebrew name. Give him this information about anyone, and he will provide an uncanny analysis of the person's character and personality.

Let me give you one example that was brought to my attention. Hakham Shabatai once cast a horoscope for an individual who was a noted philanthropist renowned for the large sums he gave to charity. After casting the horoscope, the Hakham told him that his personality contained two conflicting traits. One trait indicated that he was very generous, the other showed him to be very stingy. Hakham Shabatai told the man that even though he gave much charity, there was a constant battle whenever he did so. The philanthropist admitted that the Hakham's analysis was correct, adding that no one else had ever detected the conflict.

There are many similar stories.

Hakham Shabatai is an extraordinarily skilled astrologer, but one thing he will not do with his astrological knowledge, and that is to predict the future. There is a commandment in the Torah which states, "You shall be perfect with the Lord your God" (Deuteronomy 18:13). The Talmud interprets this as meaning that one should not go to the Chaldeans, and according to most commentators this means that one should not seek to know the future through astrology.[1] Many codifiers go so far as to count this among the 613 commandments.[2] All of these sages agree that astrology works, and that it may be used to analyze a situation if one knows the right traditions. Still, it is forbidden to use astrology to predict the future.

And so, Hakham Shabatai will use astrology to analyze an individual's personality, and even to help him solve his problems. But because of the commandment "You shall be perfect with the Lord your God," he will not use it to predict the future.

Hakham Shabatai has a wall full of books on astrology, all written in Hebrew by great Jewish sages. Many of these books are impossible to obtain today, and none of them are well known, but they all indicate that there is a strong Jewish tradition in this field. Many of these tomes tell how to cast horoscopes, while others give Kabbalistic reasons for how and why certain stars and constellations have various effects. A detailed treatment of this, however, would take us far beyond the scope of the present discussion.

Just in passing, though, it is interesting to note that Hakham Shabatai has also written a commentary on the Torah. In this book, he shows the many passages where the Torah has been interpreted in the light of astrological knowledge.

All in all, the Jewish traditions regarding astrology are very different from the ideas about astrology that prevail in the non-Jewish world. One of the most obvious differences between Jewish and non-Jewish astrology is the fact that one's Hebrew name plays a very important role in most Jewish astrological systems. This is related to the Talmudic teaching that "the name is causative."[3] The idea that one's name plays a key role in determining one's destiny is reflected in the custom of changing the name of someone who is seriously ill; it is hoped that doing so will change his destiny.

There are many other important differences between Jewish and secular astrology, but they are very technical in scope. According to Hakham Shabatai, Jewish astrology is a complex discipline that can take years to master.

From all this, we see that astrology plays a much greater role in Jewish thought than most people realize. Thus, in a number of passages, we find that the Talmud takes it for granted that astrologers can predict the future. For example, it is taught that Pharaoh's astrologers foresaw that Moses, the redeemer of Israel, would die by means of water. Thus, when his mother placed him in an ark on the Nile, they assumed that he was being sent to his doom. The Talmud says, in its account of this incident, that astrologers may predict some things, but they can never have a perfectly clear and accurate picture of the future. They may see a blurry outline; a lucid picture is beyond their grasp.[4]

Another well-known story in the Talmud has to do with Rabbi Nahman. When he was an infant, the Chaldeans (astrologers) told his mother that he would grow up to be a thief. When she asked them how this could be avoided, they told her, "Keep his head covered so that the fear of Heaven will be upon him."[5] This Talmudic anecdote is particularly well known because it provides us with one of the earliest sources for keeping our heads covered. In order to have "fear of Heaven," all male Jews wear a yarmulke at all times.

Several questions regarding astrology are discussed in our sacred texts.

The most basic question is whether or not it actually works. The great philosopher Rabbi Joseph Albo discusses this in detail, citing opposing opinions. He comes to the conclusion that the stars determine man's destiny to some extent, but it can be changed by man's free will as well as by his merit.[6]

Another often-raised question pertains to whether astrology is a science or one of the occult arts. Some maintain that it is no more than a natural science, and that anyone who has all the proper charts and tables should be able to cast an accurate horoscope. Others, however, say that charts and tables are not enough, and to obtain an accurate picture one must have a degree of divine inspiration. If one is not worthy of divine inspiration, the only way to cast an accurate horoscope is by making use of the occult arts and witchcraft, and this is forbidden by Jewish law in the strongest terms.[7]

If one delves into the texts that discuss the subject, the consensus seems to be that astrology is a combination of science and the supernatural. To some extent it is a science, and with the proper charts and tables one can cast an accurate horoscope. Without divine inspiration (*ru'ah ha-kodesh*), however, the prediction's accuracy will be limited.

There are still several points that need clarification, and the most obvious is how astrology works. Interestingly, this is discussed in a number of important Jewish texts.[8]

According to some authorities, the stars form an important link in the chain of God's providence over the world. There are many levels of interaction between God and man, the lowest being those of the angels and the stars. The Midrash teaches that "there is no blade of grass that does not have a constellation (*mazal*) over it that tells it to grow."[9] As the commentaries explain, God's providence works through angels, but the angels in turn work through the stars. As some put it, the angels are, in a sense, like souls to the stars. Thus, for example, when we speak of the stars as having intelligence, we are really speaking of the angels that are associated with them.[10]

A most important philosophical question must be asked at this point. Why are the stars necessary in the link between God and man? Why does the chain include angel, star, and man?

But before we can even discuss this question, we must pose another, even more difficult one. Why are angels necessary in the first place? Why does God have to resort to angels to carry out His commands?

This question is discussed in several important texts.[11] They explain that one of our most fundamental beliefs as Jews, and therefore one of the most basic philosophical principles, is that God is an absolute unity in every possible sense. As our great thinkers point out, there is no way in which God's essence can be analyzed; there is no way in which He can be thought of in parts.[12] We see God as a Simple Unity, absolutely simple, and absolutely One. There is no element whatsoever of plurality in Him.

But this brings up an obvious question. How can a Simple Unity interact with our multiplex world? Suppose we say that God is interacting with two men. We would then have to say that part of His mind is interacting with one man, and another part with the other. This, of course, is impossible, since it would appear to introduce an element of plurality in God. The great Jewish philosophers devoted much attention to this problem.[13]

The Kabbalists write that it is for this reason that God created spiritual worlds.[14] It is the spiritual domain that essentially interacts with man, and not God Himself. This domain could perhaps be described as an infinitely huge spiritual computer, programmed to fulfill God's one ultimate purpose, and that is to bestow good on His creation. The main difference between the spiritual domain and a computer is that its components consist of intelligent, sensitive spiritual beings. A very large portion of Kabbalah deals with the structure and interactions of the spiritual domain.

One of the spiritual domain's important components is the class of angels.

The amora R. Samuel b. Nahmani teaches that "every word emanating from God creates an angel."[15] What this means is that every word of God actually is an angel. For when we speak of God's word, we are speaking of His interaction with the world. This interaction, however, mainly involves the spiritual domain. The force that traverses this domain is what we call an angel.[16]

We have already spoken of the teaching that angels are created with every word of God. We also find that angels are created every day, since it is taught that a new troop of angels is created each morning.[17] On the other hand, there are many angels whom we know by name, such as Gabriel and Michael, who are permanent members of God's Heavenly Host. We therefore see that there are two types of angels.

This is closely related to another discussion. In the Midrash, there is a question as to when the angels were created. Some say that they were made on the second day of creation, others that they were created on the fifth day.[18]

The Kabbalists also discuss this, and many of them propose an interesting distinction. They state that there are two kinds of angels—permanent ones and temporary ones. The temporary angels were created on the second day, the permanent ones, which are likened to the birds, on the fifth. Moreover, only the permanent ones have names.[19]

The most important factors in astrology are the time and date of a person's birth. According to the Talmud, there is a "*mazal* of the hour"; in other words, the time, day, and date upon which a person is born have an important influence on his destiny.[20]

Elsewhere in the Talmud, it is taught that there is an angel called Laylah who oversees birth. It is this angel who announces whether the newborn person will be strong or weak, wise or foolish, rich or poor.[21]

Some commentators ask a serious question in this regard. The Midrash states that "one angel cannot have two missions, and two angels cannot share the same mission."[22] In the light of this important rule, which teaches us many things about the spiritual realm in general, how can a single angel oversee the birth of every individual who ever was born and who ever will be born? Does it mean that the angel who does so has many missions?

Before we can answer this question, we must first explore its logic. Why is it that one angel cannot have two missions? Why can't two angels share the same mission?

The Rambam (Maimonides) asks how angels can be differentiated. Since they have no physical shape or form, how is one angel different from another?

The answer, says the Rambam, is that angels are mostly differentiated by level. In the chain of cause and effect, one angel is higher or lower than the other, and in this respect one is closer to God while another may be farther from Him. It is in this way that they are differentiated.[23]

In another passage, however, the Rambam discusses another way that spiritual beings like angels can be differentiated.[24] All spiritual entities, angels included, are associated with physical things; differentiating them is made possible by the fact that each of them is associated with a different physical object. Thus, for example, every blade of grass has its own angel; each blade of grass is different, and so is each angel. Analogously, human souls are differentiated because they too are associated with different physical bodies.

This immediately explains why two angels cannot share a single mission. If they did, they would no longer be differentiated. There would be nothing separating them. They certainly could not be separated by space, since space does not exist in the spiritual domain, this being one of the main ways in which the spiritual domain differs from the physical. Therefore, if two angels had the same mission, they would no longer be two—by definition they would be the same angel.

This also explains why one angel cannot have two missions. For if a single angel had two missions, it would be associated with two separate physical actions. Then, however, it would be two angels, by our very definition of differentiation.

This is a very important principle. Spiritual entities like angels are primarily differentiated by virtue of their association with physical objects or actions. We therefore have a one-to-one ratio between angels and their physical counterparts.

Now let us get back to our angel called Laylah, the angel who oversees conception. This angel has overseen every conception that has ever taken place and will continue to do so for every future conception. But how can it get by without violating the rule that one angel has only one mission–the one-to-one rule?

Of course the same question applies to all the angels that have names. These are the angels that exist forever, the ones created on the fifth day. In the course of their existence, they must have many tasks and missions. We know that the angels Michael and Gabriel have many tasks. Why does the rule not hold true with regard to them?

This question is raised by Rabbenu Bahya, and he says that as long as the tasks are not radically different, one angel can have more than one mission. However, he does not explain why.[25]

So we still have to answer an important question: If a single angel has many tasks, why is it not differentiated by these tasks into many angels? How can it remain a single entity?

It appears that our question is answered by Rabbi Isaac Abarbanel, who writes that the angels are like souls to the stars.[26]

Since the human soul is also a spiritual entity, we might well ask the same question about it. How can a single soul be involved in so many tasks? Why is it not differentiated into many souls by all its tasks? But here the answer is obvious. It is integrated by its physical body. As long as the soul is associated with a single body, it can do as many different things as it pleases. Its association with the body allows it to remain an integrated whole.

The same is true of the angels that have names. These angels are like souls to the stars, and this means that the stars are their "bodies." As such, each star serves as a focus for a particular angel, maintaining it as an integrated whole even though it may have many different tasks.

This is where there is a one-to-one relationship with the named angels. Each star has its own particular angel, and each angel has its own star. This relationship allows the named angels to have many tasks and not be differentiated by them, for each named angel is integrated by the star that serves as its body.

It is now possible to explain why the permanent angels have names. The Zohar teaches that every single star in the universe has a name.[27] This is derived from the verse "He brings out their host by number, He calls them all by name" (Isaiah 40:26). It is also written, "He counts the number of the stars, He gives them each a name" (Psalms 147:4). The Midrash indicates that the different names of the stars correspond to the names of the different angels.[28] Here again we have the one-to-one relationship.

Earlier we mentioned that the named angels were created on the fifth day, whereas the unnamed, temporary angels were created on the second day. This circumstance can now be explained. The named angels had to be associated with the stars, and therefore could not be created until after the stars. Since the stars were not created until the fourth day, the angels could not be created until the fifth.

This also sheds light on the whole subject of astrology. As discussed earlier in this essay, one of the important questions pertaining to astrology asks why the stars form part of the chain between God and man. As we now see, one reason for this is because the stars are necessary so that the angels can have many tasks and still maintain their identity.

Another question asks how angels interact with each other, and here we encounter the same difficulties as in the question about the differentiation of angels. We know, however, that angels interact with each other in planning future events, and indeed, that this is an important part of their task. Apparently the relationships between the various stars and planets are involved as well. Especially important is the way they appear when viewed from the earth, since this is the focus of their activity. The way the astronomical bodies are arrayed in our line of sight seems to be a major factor in the interaction.

In the final analysis, then, astrology can offer some important insights into Jewish theology. At first it may be somewhat difficult to understand how the stars have the power to influence man, but as we probe more deeply into our classical texts, these questions open many other doors and enable us to understand other concepts more deeply.

NOTES

1. Pesahim 113b, *Yoreh De'ah* 179:1. For further discussion on this and related matters, see *She'elot u-Teshuvot ha-Rashba ha-Meyuhasot leha-Ramban* 283, *Teshuvot ha-Rashba* 1:413, *Teshuvot ha-Rivash* 92, *Bet Yosef*, *Yoreh De'ah* 179.

2. Ramban, additions to *Sefer ha-Mizvot*, positive commandment 8; *Sefer Mizvot Katan* 10.

3. Berakhot 7b.

4. Sotah 12b.

5. Shabbat 156b.

6. *Ikkarim* 4:4. This is also the opinion of Tosafot to Shabbat 156a, s.v. *ein*. Many writers take it for granted that Maimonides did not believe in astrology at all, basing this on what he writes in *Yad, Avodat Kokhavim* 11:16 and *Moreh Nevukhim* 3:37. Elsewhere, however, he appears to admit that it can predict the future at least to some degree; see *Yad, Yesodei ha-Torah* 10:3.

7. This is discussed at length in *Ha-Kotev* on *Ein Yaakov*, Shabbat 156a.

8. See Bahya and Abarbanel on Deuteronomy 18:14, *Derekh ha-Shem* 2:7.

9. *Bereshit Rabbah* 10:6, Zohar 2:80b.

10. *Or ha-Shem* 4:4. See *Sha'ar Rashbi* (Tel Aviv, 5721) on *Perek Shirah* (p. 299).

11. Most notably by Rabbi Zadok ha-Kohen of Lublin, in his *Sihat Malakhei he-Sharet*.

12. *Yad, Yesodei ha-Torah* 1:7.

13. See Rabbi Levi ben Gershon, *Milhamot ha-Shem* 3.

14. See *Pardes Rimmonim* 2:6.

15. Hagigah 14a (but Rav and Samuel apparently disagree; see ibid. and see below).

16. Cf. *Moreh Nevukhim* 2:6.

17. Hagigah 14a, *Bereshit Rabbah* 78:1.

18. *Bereshit Rabbah* 1:3, 3:8; *Shemot Rabbah* 15:22; *Tanhuma Hayyei Sarah* 3; *Midrash Tehillim* 24, 86, 104; *Pirkei Rabbi Eliezer* 4. See Rabbi Judah Barceloni on *Sefer Yezirah*, p. 187.

19. *Bahir* 21. See Radal on *Pirkei Rabbi Eliezer* 4:1, from Zohar 1:17b, 1:18b, 1:34a, 1:46b. Also see Radal on *Pirkei Rabbi Eliezer* 4:11. Bahya on Genesis 28:12 reverses this, stating that permanent angels were created on the second day, temporary angels on the fifth.

20. Shabbat 156a.

21. Niddah 16b.

22. *Bereshit Rabbah* 50:2, Rashi on Genesis 18:2. *Moreh Nevukhim* 2:6.

23. *Yad, Yesodei ha-Torah* 2:5.

24. *Moreh Nevukhim,* introduction to pt. 2, no. 16. See *Or ha-Shem* 1:1:16; *Shefa'Tal* 1:3 (Hanau, 5372), p. 13c in bottom note; *Pardes Rimmonim* 2:7; *Amud ha-Avodah, Vikua'h Shoel u-Meshiv* 99. For a more detailed discussion, see my *God, Man and Tefillin* (New York: National Council of Synagogue Youth, 1973), p. 42.

25. Bahya on Genesis 18:2.

26. Abarbanel on Deuteronomy 18:24. See also *Perush* on *Yad, Yesodei ha-Torah* 2:5.

27. Zohar 3:269a.

28. *Bereshit Rabbah* 78:4, *Yefeh To'ar* ad loc., *Shemot Rabbah* 48:2, *Bemidmar Rabbah* 11:7, *Tanhuma Vayakhel* 4.

Chapter 5
Male and Female

Many have wondered about the differences between man and woman as expressed in the Halakhah. Some have attempted to explain them in terms of the psychological and social differences between the sexes, but so little is really known about these differences that this is little more than speculation. Moreover, the Torah deals primarily with the spiritual human being, and when we find differentiation between man and woman, it is primarily because of their spiritual differences.

In order to understand these spiritual differences, we must also seek to comprehend the purpose of God's creation of two sexes. After all, both sexes partake of God's "image," as it is written, "God created man in His image, in the image of God He created him, male and female He created them" (Genesis 1:27).[1]

The key to this lies in the teaching of our sages that when a man and woman live together in holiness, the Divine Presence rests between them. The Hebrew word for "man," *ish,* contains the letter *yud,* while *ishah,* "woman," contains a *heh.* These are the first two letters of God's Name.[2] Man therefore corresponds to the *yud* in God's Name, and woman corresponds to the *heh.*

The Masters teach us that the *yud* alludes to wisdom, while the *heh* corresponds to understanding. Wisdom is thus the male element, and understanding, the female.[3]

The Baal Shem Tov further teaches us that the *yud* in God's Name is His gift of creation, while the *heh* is the Hand that gives it. The gematria, or numerical value, of *heh* is 5, corresponding to the five fingers.[4]

Wisdom is particularly related to beginnings and the past, as it is written, "The beginning is wisdom" (Proverbs 4:7). It is furthermore written, "I am first, and I am last" (Isaiah 44:6). The Masters teach us that "first" refers to wisdom, and "last" to understanding.[5]

Wisdom, the masculine element, is therefore the past, and understanding, the female element, is the future. Wisdom consists of all that one has accumulated, while understanding is how one will make use of it.

Man's element, therefore, is primarily the past, and woman's, the future.

Knowledge is the interface between wisdom and understanding, between past and future, between male and female. It is thus written, "And Adam *knew* Eve his wife" (Genesis 4:1).[6]

The past influences the future, but the future cannot change the past. Knowledge is what the past interjects into the future. It comes essentially from the male element, and thus we are taught that "woman's knowledge is light."[7] Since understanding is the female element, we are also taught that "greater understanding was given to woman."[8]

The six weekdays are masculine in this sense, while the Sabbath is feminine.[9] During the six weekdays, the world is renewed through the original momentum of creation, and therefore they pertain to the past. But on the Sabbath we partake of the world-to-come—the ultimate future—the world when all will be Sabbath.

We can now understand the basic differentiation between man and woman in the Torah. Man's obligations are directed toward the past, while woman is directed toward the future. Man preserves the past, woman creates the future.

The study of Torah relates to the teachings of the past, and for this reason is primarily man's obligation. Women are not obligated to study, except insofar as they must know enough to keep the commandments.[10] Preserving the past through Torah study is the domain of the male.

When the Torah was first given, however, it was taught to the women first. It is written, "Thus shall you say to the house of Jacob"—the women—"and tell the sons of Israel" (Exodus 19:3).[11] When the Torah was first given, it represented the entire future of the Jewish people and therefore pertained more to women than to men.

Besides this, there is also a Torah that is specifically feminine. It is written, "Hear, my son, the teaching of your father, and do not abandon the Torah of your mother" (Proverbs 1:8). Our sages teach us that "teaching of your father" refers to the Torah given at Sinai, while "Torah of your mother" refers to customs that would be innovated in the *future*. It is this verse that gives us an obligation to abide by such customs.[12]

The most important difference between man and woman, however, is also the most obvious. This is the fact that women bear children and men do not. It is in this role that women are primarily responsible for creating the future of the human race. Hannah was speaking for all women when she said, "Master of the universe, You created no part of my body in vain.... You created these breasts upon my heart to nourish my young."[13]

There are two basic categories of commandments in the Torah. The positive commandments tell us "Do," and the negative commandments tell us "Do not do." The Torah teaches that negative commandments are binding on men and women equally. The same is true of positive commandments that do not depend on a specific time.[14]

It is in the realm of positive commandments dependent on time that the major difference between the halakhic obligations of men and women lies. The practical effect of this rule is to exempt women from seven commandments: the *Shema*, the head *tefillin* and the hand *tefillin* (two separate commandments), *zizzit*, *sukkah*, *lulav*, and *shofar*.[15]

This distinction is related to the basic elements of male and female, namely, past and future. Positive commandments impel us into action, and thus represent the past pressing into the future. Negative commandments, on the other hand, hold us back, and they represent the future holding back the past. Positive commandments, therefore, pertain to the masculine element, while negative commandments pertain to the feminine.[16]

Since the past influences the future, men must keep the negative commandments just as women do. In influencing the future, they too enter the feminine domain. The future, however, cannot change the past, and therefore, where time is involved, women are exempt from positive commandments. Where the commandment does not involve time, however, future blends with past, and women are also obligated.[17]

It is in their ability to bear children and create life that women fulfill the totality of the 248 positive commandments. This is why *rehem*, the Hebrew word for "womb," has the gematria, or numerical value, of 248, the totality of the positive commandments.[18]

Still, one may ask, why the inequality? We find that in many ways the Torah seems to give man a superior status or a dominant position.[19] This stance may be related to our earlier observation that the masculine past determines and dominates the future, while the feminine future cannot change the past. Nevertheless, we must seek to understand the reason for this inequality.

In discussing the basic inequality with regard to women, we must distinguish between man's situation before Adam's fall and after. Before the sin, it is written, "Fill the earth and dominate it [her]" (Genesis 1:28). Our sages teach us that this means that the man dominates the woman.[20] In dominating the earth, and in thus being preeminent in commerce and industry, man also dominates the woman, who is dependent on him.

After the sin, however, God told woman, "Your desire shall be directed to your man, and he shall rule over you" (Genesis 3:16).[21] What had previously been no more than a slight advantage, because life in Eden had not required work, now became absolute dominance. As a result of the sin, man was cursed, "By the sweat of your brow you shall eat bread" (Genesis 3:19). Both man and woman became much more dependent on the man's work, and the male role became correspondingly more important.

To some degree, this happened because woman was the first of the human pair to disobey God's word. As the one who had "light knowledge," she was enticed to partake of the Tree of Knowledge.[22]

But the questions remain: Why was there a basic inequality between man and woman? Why was man dominant even before the sin? Why was the woman enticed, and why was the commandment not to eat of the Tree of Knowledge only given to the man?

We find an allusion to this problem in the verse "And God made two great lights, the great light to rule the day, and the small light to rule the night" (Genesis 1:16). Our sages teach us that the sun and moon were originally created equal. The moon complained, saying, "It is impossible for two equal kings to rule under one crown." God therefore told the moon, "Go and reduce yourself."[23]

The Zohar, the most authoritative mystical text, teaches us that the moon's reduction symbolizes the subordinate status of the feminine element in all creation.[24]

The moon lost the power of radiating its own light and now only reflects the light of the sun.

The sun is responsible for the measure of years, which is a simple repeating cycle. The very word for "year," *shanah*, means "repetition." The sun is therefore the masculine element, repeating the past.

The moon, on the other hand, measures months. The Hebrew word for "month" is *hodesh*, literally meaning "something new." The lunar month is based on the phases of the moon, going through a complete cycle of birth, growth, and death, and constantly anticipating the future.[25]

The moon complained that the masculine past and the feminine future had been created with equal influence. God reduced the influence of the future, thus reducing the feminine element.

The reason man has dominion over the earth is that he can learn from past experience. This link with the past is also why he dominates woman.

The future world, however, will be a time when all is Sabbath, and as the prophet foretold, "The light of the moon will be like the light of the sun" (Isaiah 30:26). At that time, the inequality between man and woman will likewise be eradicated.[26]

We are rapidly approaching the Messianic Age, when the curse associated with Adam's sin will be removed.[27] Once the curse is eliminated, woman's status will also change profoundly. Our sages thus teach us, "All will be healed, except for the serpent."[28] This change in woman's status may be alluded to in the prophecy "For God will create a new thing, a woman shall court a man" (Jeremiah 31:22).[29]

The new awareness among women is merely a glimpse of the light of the future Messianic Age.[30] We already see this illumination in such things as the rebirth of Israel and the return of Jerusalem, as well as in the renewed quest for peace, justice, honest government, equality, and meaning in life. We also see it in the technological advances that, to a large measure, have eliminated the curse of Adam.

Rapid technological and sociological changes bring great social upheavals in their wake. The cataclysmic changes which take place as the end draws near will result in considerable dislocation and suffering, often referred to as the *hevlei mashi'ah*, "the birthpangs of the Messiah."[31] Many people will fall away from Judaism, and it will be a time of great godlessness.[32]

We can use the glimmer of light shining into our times from the future Messianic Age to strengthen our commitment to the light of Torah. If, on the other hand, we try to use this glimmer to fight against the greater light of Torah, then we will have neither.

If we let the Torah light our way, we will be worthy of the world of the future—the world where all is Sabbath—when "the light of the moon will be like the light of the sun."

NOTES

1. See Recanati, Bahya, *Tiferet Yonatan*, and Hirsch ad loc.; Zohar 3:117a.

2. Rashi on Sotah 17a, s.v. *Shekhinah*.

3. See Zohar 3:290a.

4. See *Mevasser Zedek, Re'eh*, quoted in *Sefer Baal Shem Tov, Re'eh* 8.

5. Ra'avad and Ramban on *Sefer Yezirah* 1:5. See Avot 3:17, R. Yonah, *Derekh Hayyim* (Maharal) ad loc.

6. See *Ez Hayyim, Sha'ar ha-Kelipot* 2; *Likkutei Amarim* (*Tanya*) 1:3 (7b).

7. Shabbat 33b, Kiddushin 80b, *Tanhuma*, *Va'era* 22; Zohar 2:218a. See below, n. 22.

8. Niddah 45b, *Bereshit Rabbah* 18:1. Cf. *Bereshit Rabbah* 34:9, Tosafot to Ketubot 50a, s.v. *u-bat*.

9. This may be hinted at in *Bereshit Rabbah* 11:8, Zohar 2:63b.

10. Kiddushin 29b, *Yoreh De'ah* 246:6. Cf. Sotah 3:4 (20a).

11. *Shemot Rabbah* 28:2, *Pirkei Rabbi Eliezer* 41.

12. Pesahim 50b. On women's role in teaching Torah to their children, see Radal on *Shemot Rabbah* 28:2, no. 5.

13. Berakhot 31b.

14. Kiddushin 1:7 (29a). Cf. *Abudraham, Seder Tefillot shel Hol*, pp. 25, 41; *Kol Bo* 73.

15. See *Sefer ha-Mizvot*, end of positive commandment 248. See also positive commandments 10, 12, 13, 14, 168, 169, 170. Other commandments from which women are exempt include Torah study (11), writing a Torah (18), having children (212), marriage (213), staying home from war during the first year of marriage (214), circumcision (215), and the priestly blessing (26).

16. Zohar 1:48b, *Ez Hayyim, Sha'ar Kelipot Nogah* 5, ed. Ashlag, p. 397. See next note.

17. Time-dependent positive commandments are rooted in "hidden love" where the future element (*imah*) is completely concealed. Non-time-dependent commandments, on the other hand, are rooted in "revealed love," where the future is revealed to some extent. *Ez Hayyim, Sha'ar Kizur ABYA* 4, *Shemonah Sha'arim, Sha'ar ha-Mizvot*, introduction (Tel Aviv: Ashlag, 5722), pp. 4–5; *Nahar Shalom* (Tel Aviv: Ashlag, 5720), pp. 64, 67.

18. Cf. *Tikkunei Zohar* 30 (74), *Pardes Rimmonim* 23:13.

19. See Horayot 3:7 (13a), *Yoreh De'ah* 252:8 in *vagah*.

20. Rashi ad loc., *Bereshit Rabbah* 8:12, Yevamot 6:6 (65b), Bertinoro ad loc. See Kiddushin 2b, Nazir 59b.

21. Rashi and *Gur Aryeh* (Maharal) ad loc. Cf. *Yad, Ishut* 15:20.

22. *Pirkei Rabbi Eliezer* 13 (32a), Rashi on Genesis 3:15. See above, n. 7.

23. Rashi ad loc., Hullin 60b, *Pirkei Rabbi Eliezer* 6.

24. Zohar 2:147b, *Tikkunei Zohar* 36 (71b), *Pardes Rimmonim* 18:1. See Genesis 37:9–10, *Midrash Tehillim* 148:1.

25. See Ra'avad on *Sefer Yezirah* 1:5, *Pardes Rimmonim* 18:3.

26. See Radal on *Pirkei Rabbi Eliezer* 45 (107a), n. 22.

27. *Milhamot ha-Shem* (Ramban) 45. On the world's future perfection, see *Bereshit Rabbah* 12:6, 95:1, *Yeshui'ot Meshiho* (Abarbanel) 3:6 (55b), *Avodat ha-Kodesh* 2:38.

28. *Bereshit Rabbah* 20:5, from Isaiah 65:25.

29. Or: "a woman shall turn into a man." See Rashi ad loc., *Midrash Tehillim* 73:4, Zohar 1:257a.

30. *Kuzari* 4:23.

31. Sanhedrin 98b, *Netzah Yisrael* (Maharal) 36.

32. *Sihot ha-Ran* 35, 126, 220; *Kokhavei Or*, p. 97 (n. 19).

Appendix

A Theological Reflection on Death, Resurrection, and the Age of the Universe

The following is a translation of a sermon preached by Rabbi Is-rael Lipschitz in the German-Polish city of Danzig (Gdansk) in 5602 (1842) on the subject of life after death, the resurrection of the dead, and the age of the universe—all subjects taken up by Rabbi Kaplan in the articles included in this collection. The sermon itself is referred to by Rabbi Kaplan in "The Age of the Universe" (see above, pp. 8 and 26 n. 15), and the Association felt it appropriate to include a translation of this pioneering work in the volume. We thank Dr. Yaakov Elman for undertaking this task.

Derush Or ha-Hayyim:
A Theological Reflection on Death, Resurrection and the Age of the Universe

by

Rabbi Israel Lipschitz

(translated and annotated by Yaakov Elman)

Contents

Introduction

R. Israel Lipschitz (Lipschuetz, Lipschutz) (1782-1860), best-known as the author of the *Tif'eret Yisrael* commentary on the Mishnah, was the son of R. Gedaliah b. Israel Lipschitz, who served as rabbi in Emden and Chodsiezen. R. Israel served at Wronke (Polish Vronik, Wronki), from at least as early as 1818,[1] and possibly as early as 1812.[2] He also succeeded his father in Chodziesen (Polish Chodziez, known as Kolmar after 1877[3]), serving there from 1826, when his father died, to 1837,[4] when he was elected rabbi of Danzig (Polish Gdansk) and its surrounding communities (Weinberg, Old Schottland and Langfuhr). In between he spent some time in Dessau, but it is not clear just how long he was there. Thus he spent most of his rabbinic career not more than 240 km north and west of Poznan; Dessau is some 200 km west southwest of that city, Wronki is 50 km to the west northwest, Chodziesen is some 62 km to the north, and Danzig some 240 km to the north northeast.

Until his death in 1860, he served in Danzig where he represented strict Orthodoxy, but was known as a community activist and ascetic.[5] As his fame spread, his grave in Stolzenberger Friedhof was visited by *Ostjuden*, according to one report.[6]

Despite historians' negative assessment of his influence on the Danzig community, the sermon presented below shows him to have been alive to the religious problems of the community, and aware of the wider currents of scientific discovery and the doctrinal problems these brought.

He is best known for his monumental and widely used commentary on the Mishnah, popularly known as *Tif'eret Yisrael*, included in standard editions of *Mishnayot.* The *Tif'eret Yisrael* is known for its brevity and its sensitivity to the plain meaning of the text. In his introductions to various orders and tractates, such as his masterful *Kalkelet Shabbat* on the Sabbath laws, Rabbi Lipschitz also shows his ability to organize large amounts of complex halakhic material.

Rabbi Lipschitz also published a brief commentary to the Mishnah entitled *Zera Yisrael* (Vilna, 1852); his ethical will was published in Königsberg in 1861.[7] His son reports that his father had composed notes on Talmud, on Maimonides and on Shulhan Arukh, and many responsa,[8] all of which remain unpublished, as do his sermons but for the one translated here. He also composed a commentary on Avot (*Rashei Avot*) and a work entitled *Megilat Setarim.*

Rabbi Lipschitz was known for his piety, but, living under the shadow of the Haskalah and the Reform movement, he showed himself remarkably open to new ideas, demonstrating a willingness to appropriate useful discoveries in his work and thought, as we shall see below.

In the following sermon, which is included in editions of his commentary to the Mishnah and is usually found after Tractate Sanhedrin, Rabbi Lipschitz displays his knowledge of the geological and paleontological discoveries made in the first half of the nineteenth century, discussing, among other things, dinosaur fossils and the mammoth remains found in Siberia and near Baltimore. He relates all this to the midrashim and to kabbalistic teachings regarding the age of the universe,[9] and proposes several striking interpretations of the first verses of Genesis in the light of this association.

Aside from this topic, Rabbi Lipschitz used his knowledge of science to mitigate any doubts his congregants had regarding life after death and the resurrection of the dead in Messianic times.

It is of interest to note that he mentions two authorities in the course of his sermon, one a Dr. Hufeland (Christoph Wilhelm Hufeland, 1762-1836), who popularized some of the new discoveries in paleontology for his own purposes, and Dr.

Cuvier (George Leopold Cuvier (1769-1832)), one of the great names of the age and of the history of paleontology and zoology. While the latter wrote in French, Rabbi Lipschitz almost certainly read him in a German translation or popularization (see below).

It is worth noting that while Rabbi Lipschitz seems to speak of an evolutionary scheme of zoological development in his description of the ages of the earth, it is more likely that he followed Cuvier in his theory of "catastrophism" or "cataclysmic theory." As he put it,

> Life on earth has been frequently interrupted by frightful events. Innumerable organisms have become the victims of such catastrophes. Invading waters have swallowed up the inhabitants of dry land; the sudden rise of the sea bottom has deposited aquatic animals on land. Their species have vanished forever; they have left behind only sparse remains, which the naturalist is currently striving to interpret.

However, this did not require a new creation for these replacement species. In opposing Lamarck's theory of the inheritance of acquired characteristics, a controversy which lasted decades, Cuvier stressed the lack of evidence for change in species, and rejected proto-evolutionary schemes. On the other hand, though a convinced Protestant, Cuvier stressed that he did by no means assert

> the necessity of a new creation for living species; I say only that they did not live in the places we now find them. They must therefore have come in from other regions.[10]

Others took the next step of ascribing the new, superior creations to God, and it was this variety of catastrophism which Cuvier followed, perhaps under the influence of the fourth edition of Hufeland's work (see below).

Rabbi Lipschitz's sermon is devoted to these themes, as well as the problem of the age of the universe, which had become a hotly-debated matter during his lifetime. Because of the length of Rabbi Lipschitz's disquisition, readers may find the table of contents above helpful.

***

Derush Or ha-Hayyim:
A Theological Reflection on Death,
Resurrection and the Age of the Universe

The following is a sermon preached by Rabbi Israel Lipschitz, author of the *Tif'eret Yisrael* commentary on the Mishnah, on Shabbat Hol ha-Mo'ed 5702.

[12]I, I am He Who comforts you.
Who are you that you fear mortal man,
    mortals who fare like grass?
[13]Have you forgotten God your Maker,
    Who stretched out the skies,
        made firm the earth?
You live all day in constant dread
    of the rage of the oppressor,
        preparing to cut you down.
But where is the rage of the oppressor?
[14]Quickly the crouching one is freed,
    he will not die for the Pit;
        he will not want for good.
[15]For I am God your Lord,
    Who calms the sea
        and the roaring waves;
God of Hosts is His Name.
           (Isaiah 51:12-15)[11]

The Challenge of Death*

Tanna deBe Eliyahu: "The righteous whom God will in
the future restore to life will not return to their dust, as
[Scripture] states: 'He will call him holy, all who are written
for life in Jerusalem'[12]—just as the Holy One exists forever,
so too they will exist forever. And if you ask, what will the
righteous do at the time of the terrible destruction of the
world, during those years when the Holy One, blessed be
He, renews His world? The Holy One, blessed be He, produces eagles' wings for them, and they drift upon the face
of the waters, as [Scripture] states, 'Therefore we will not
fear when the earth is changed, though mountains topple
into the sea.'[13] And if you say that they will feel pain, [Scrip-
ture] states, 'Those whose hope is in God will gain strength,
they will lift wing like an eagle, and run without becoming
weary, they shall march and not grow faint' "[14] (Sanhedrin
92a).[15]

The Benefits of Facing Death Squarely

Mortal man, perpetually suspended between life and death,
must always be aware of his situation, if he wants to succeed in
both heaven[ly] and earth[ly matters] and on earth. Nevertheless, [it is heavenly] life that he must consider more carefully;
that is, he must never forget his eternal existence for a moment.
He must always consider himself as an eternally existent being,
one who will live forever, as the verse states, "I have placed
before you life and death,"[16] viz., I have placed your death and
life under your own care—but "choose life,"[17] choose eternal
life and keep [this goal] in sight with great care. O my brothers,
note that we are commanded by our holy Torah and our sages,
may their memory be blessed, to look on death, our greatest
enemy, with a tranquil heart. Often, even every moment, we

*Headings are not by Rabbi Lipschitz, but have been added to aid the
reader.

must imagine ourselves at our last hour, when we are separated from [our] earth[ly existence], as it is said: "Unwillingly you die."[18]

[The same matter is expressed] by our sages, may their memory be blessed, in Shabbat 153a: "Repent one day before your death," [to which] the question was asked, "Does then a person know the day of his death?" and they answered, "Let him repent today lest he die tomorrow." We ourselves might still ask why our sages suggest that a person may die "tomorrow"—are we then sure of today?

However, [our sages] had two reasons for using this expression.

(1) Because a person on his last day [on earth] can act only in confusion and perplexity, and so too his repentance comes at a time when he is not himself.

(2) Because human beings, who tend to disregard serious matters, will think, "Is it possible that I will die today? I don't yet feel the slightest touch of death on my body!" Therefore our true friends [i.e., the sages] have told us very calmly, "Let it be as you say. Nevertheless, repent today lest you die tomorrow. [After all,] anything can happen in a day. Is it not written, 'In a night it came into being, and in a night it was destroyed'?"[19]

But this thought of death [that I advise you] to keep before you is of great benefit to the body and the soul. For the body—since in this way the person will minimize the pain [occasioned by] his [material] needs, and put in proper perspective the honor [others] grant him in this world; he will say to himself, "Why should I bother myself regarding this dreamworld, from which I must depart perforce?" [In this way] his [material desires and connections] will not impede his departure from [this world].

A second benefit to the body will be to increase his faith and trust in the Holy One, blessed be He, as our sages, may they be blessed, said (in Hullin 5b) [regarding the verse] "Man and beast will God redeem"[20]—the Holy One, blessed be He, redeems only the man who makes himself as a beast [in not feeling the hurt of insult or the pleasure of honor paid him].

Furthermore, a third benefit [that comes of] always keeping [before him] the image of himself in his last hour [is that] the fear of death will be stilled; he will not be overcome with panic when he reaches his end, and will prepare himself in tranquility for death at any moment.

However, the benefit that accrues to his soul by [his] remembering his destiny will be much greater, for this will blunt the force of his [evil] inclination, and all the pride and arrogance which lead him to sin. He will be humbled in heart, and be kept from infringing on the sacred [commands] of our holy Torah, viz., the laws whose rationale is hidden from humanity, and the holy secrets, for he will always remember the great loss which may occur to him in the world of eternity if he does not keep the commands of God his Lord.

Keeping Track of Time

It is for this reason that the psalmist beseeched [God] "to number our days, and so inform [us]."[21] The word *ken* ["so"] seems similar to [its use] in the verse "Truly [*ken*] do the daughters of Zelophehod speak."[22] It indicates intensity or strength, as in "the washbasin and its stand [*kanno*],"[23] that is, all know that they will die, and explicitly admit that they will die. Thus they are aware that their days are numbered—and despite [this awareness] they [continue] to sin! [The psalmist] informs us that we should count [our days] with intense awareness that every day of our lives which passes brings us imperceptibly to another world. I will thus become aware in my inmost heart, and know that in the end I will see the Face of God; "let me bring to You, O God, a wise heart."[24]

This is one of the reasons our holy Torah commanded us to count the Omer,[25] namely, just as the Holy Nation counts seven weeks from its birth [as a nation], that is, from the day of the Exodus from Egypt until they merited Divine revelation at Sinai, so too now must you divide your life into seven sevenths, from the day of your birth to the time that all flesh shall come to bow before the Lord, God of Hosts,[26] when He appears to him on the last day of his life, as [Scripture] states, "every knee shall bend,"[27] and as [Scripture] states, "from when the scythe begins [cutting] the standing grain,"[28] viz., from the day that the scythe of the evil inclination begins to strike at your soul, that is, from the time of your birth. From then you must begin to count seven "weeks," namely, seven times seven years.

This is because a person's life changes every seven years, and his obligations increase and become greater than before. (1) At the end of the first seven years a person is weaned from his early years of childhood, and he is then required to [cooperate] in being trained [to perform his religious duties], and his parents are obliged to direct their child in the service of God more than hitherto. (2) At the beginning of his fourteenth year he is a *bar mitzvah* and is obligated by Sinaitic law (as in *Responsa of the Rosh*, no. 16) to perform all the mitzvot of the Torah. (3) At the beginning of his twenty-first year the Heavenly Court [begins to] exact punishment [for his misdeeds] ([*Numbers*] *Rabbah Korah*, and Shabbat 89b) since our intellects are then fully developed, and Heaven then examines our deeds far more carefully. (4) At the end of the fourth seven-year period, our bodies are fully developed and we are in the prime of life; [hence the Mishnah states] "at thirty for strength," since we are accepted in the company of adults, and are more experienced in life's vicissitudes and our obligation to carry the yoke of worldly affairs in an ethical and righteous manner. (5) At the end of the fifth seven-year period, we have already traversed half our allotted span of seventy years. (6) At the end of our fiftieth year is our jubilee, our minds are at the peak of their powers but the body begins its decline; you stand at the crossroads, and there stands your good mother, the holy Torah, and calls out to you: "Count for yourself," "and you shall count for yourselves"; "for your personal good and for society's good—begin the count of the days of your life." "Man, are you still sunk in your drunken concern for the affairs of this transitory world? Awake, awake! Your blood has now cooled, your intellect has matured, and your [physical] drives are slowly declining. You yourself see your life-force decline, you now know that you cannot continue indefinitely, and therefore, 'Sanctify the fiftieth year.'[29] Now at least you can begin to worry about the sustenance of your soul in the other world which you now approach, the time is very close!"

Keeping Sight of Important Matters

And as we accustom ourselves to think constantly in this manner, the failing well of death itself and our awareness of it, light and life are elevated. Nevertheless, we are commanded to examine our lives, viz., our eternal lives, with an even sharper eye, for this will elevate our emotions, and [the thought of death nearby] will allow us to appreciate the true worth of man, the importance of life, what weight and importance he has. If [his soul] does not continue to exist after [his body's death], that will be more ignoble than death itself, for the living know that they will die, but the dead know nothing.[30] However, the glory of God, may He be blessed, is that within the dark cloud of death He allows hidden sparks of light to shine, "God proposed to dwell in darkness"[31]—the Holy One, blessed be He, wished to hide the precious light of eternal life and to obscure it in darkness so that man will not clearly apprehend the mode of this life [which ends in death]. This was [done] in order not to infringe on man's free will, for that is the purpose of the creation of man in the world; through his [exercise of] free will he will succeed.

The [true] situation is obscure. Nevertheless, a little of that light will enlighten our eyes, and despite the great hiddenness of our true situation, we may thank God that we have [the opportunity] for eternal life.

Life After Death and the Resurrection of the Dead

We have perceived all this from You, our Father in Heaven, as [Scripture] states: "You will teach me the path of life, in Your

presence is perfect joy; delights are ever in Your right hand"[32]—
for we will live there with You, "With You is the source of life;
by Your light do we see light"[33]—true light.

Belief in this basic principle of faith brings benefits to the
body and to the soul. To the body: How can the body find eating, drinking, and other pleasures pleasant if the person knows
in his soul that he is like a sheep being led to the slaughter[34] and
in the end his soul will dissipate like a cloud? To the soul, however, there is no greater benefit, for in this temporal life it is
often seen that a righteous person is destroyed in his righteousness, while a wicked person succeeds in his wickedness,[35] and
because of this people become weakened in their faith, not
following the Torah's path at the cost of the loss of material
pleasures, money, or honor. But the belief in the survival of the
soul will be a light [to him] in his path in this world, in his knowledge that there is a place of reward and punishment, since in
this world this is impossible without infringement on his free
will. How much will belief in this principle help him even in his
last hour, when it will sweeten the bitterness of death for him!

However, even if the principle is well rooted in the hearts
of my beloved listeners, nevertheless I think that every Jewish
heart will rejoice at having strong and well-founded proofs
regarding this principle without which any bliss whatsoever is
impossible in this world.

[Indeed,] even Joshua sent two spies to search out the praiseworthy land, even though the Holy One, blessed be He, assured
him that it was a land flowing with milk and honey, and [that]
they [i. e. the Israelites] would be able to conquer it; we too should
send our two spies—our senses and our intellects—to the most
praiseworthy "land of [eternal] life" in order to strengthen our
hearts in this precious principle of faith.

However, my beloved brothers, this principle of faith en-
compasses two aspects. (1) Every Jew is obliged to believe that
his soul will not be obliterated after his death; (2) everyone is
obliged as well to believe that there will be a bodily resurrection.

The twofold aspect of resurrection is hinted at by the doubled verses in our prayers: "The dead will God bring to life in His great lovingkindness,"[36] that is, in future times God will revive the soul and it will in the end live again within the body. So too it is written, "With length of days will I satisfy him and I will show him My salvation,"[37] [which we recite twice, referring to] length of days in the world of souls [after death] and bodily length of days [after the resurrection] And so too "Every soul will praise God, Hallelujah!" [which is also recited twice, refers] to spirit and body. These words are repeated three times in our prayers in order firmly to implant this principle in our hearts, [this principle] without which there is no joy or success in this world.

Therefore, O my elder brothers, do not tremble when you see your strength failing and that you are approaching the goal of all men; know that man's life will not be obliterated. We will live and not cease from existing for all time. May God strengthen my feeble powers to enlighten you, and may He strengthen your own powers to be enlightened! Listen and be consoled!

This daily consideration has three aspects.

(1) We wish to make clear that our souls, that is, the chain of our thoughts, will continue without end even after our deaths.

(2) We wish also to clarify the situation of the soul after death, and how the essence of the unrighteous may cease [despite the soul's eternity]

(3) In the end we wish to clarify also that the body will once again live a natural life in this world.

I. Proofs for the Survival of the Soul After Death

The belief in the survival of the soul lies before us as clear as the sun. For it we have five simple and strong proofs. They are (1) from our own experience, (2) from the world in general, (3) from [God's] creations in particular, (4) from the Holy One, blessed be He, Himself, (5) from our holy Torah, which puts its stamp on this belief, the stamp of the Holy One, blessed be He, which is Truth.

Now we will explain all these aforementioned proofs, one by one.

From Experience

1. From our own experience. All our activities and preoccupations, thoughts and speech—all of them are pursued as though we are certain that we will live forever. We habitually speak of our deaths [with confidence], and not only when we are calm and at peace, but even when we are being entertained and are enjoying ourselves, we are capable [of contemplating our deaths] at that very moment of filling our mouths with joy,[38] as though we were to speak of [a mere] change of clothes. Is not this [inner certainty], then, a reliable sign for the [validity] of this belief, this call from the soul which sees further than fleshly eyes, and which whispers to us: "O man, do not fear, you will not die and remain dead forever"?

This is what the psalmist says as his soul soars to the heights in the throes of his prophetic inspiration, "I will not die,"[39] and even if this one which we call death touches me, "rather will I live,"[40] that is to say, I will only then begin my true life.

For if the thick fleshly cover should peel away, I will see with open eyes and "I will recount the deeds of God"[41]—I will comprehend the secrets of the universe and the secret of the Torah's laws, which remain closed off to mortals, whose vision is blocked in this material world; then, however, the cloud will lift and I will see the true light.

But death itself is called "slight suffering," and for that reason [the psalmist] says, "God has afflicted me"[42]—then, at the time of death, He has caused me a little pain, "but He has not given me over to death"[43]—entirely [hefker], though it is in His power to wipe me out altogether.

Therefore [the verse says,] "Open for me the Gates of Righteousness,"[44] that I shall walk in the way of righteousness which our holy Torah has set forth, "and I shall enter them,"[45] as God has taught me, and then will I surely know that a time will come when "I shall praise God" Who created death, as was written in the Torah [scroll] of R. Meir, "God saw all He had made, and behold, death was good [instead of "it was very good"],[46] for there will the righteous person eat the fruit of his deeds; "he will enter with song, carrying his sheaves."[47]

The fear of death, too, will not make me tremble, for "this is the Gate to God, the righteous will enter it,"[48] that is, that which humans term "death" is the gate through which and in which one passes into God's [Heavenly] Temple, pleasantly passing the time in the Presence of the Living God; the righteous will enter therein, with soulful peace and a courageous heart, without fear or panic, for that is the gate of light to eternal success, to be lit with the light of life.

This is, then, the proof of eternal life from one's own experience.

From the World as a Whole

2. However, aside from [the proof to be derived from] our own feelings and thoughts, we can establish that we will not expire [eternally] nor be obliterated forever, as we said, from the world as a whole; for if we carefully consider nature and its activities in general, as it continues on its round, we will see that what seems like death itself establishes a new life; every fall on one side is a rise on another, and every bit of decay and corruption which seems to exert dominion over [nature's] creatures brings forth a new creation.[49]

Nature changes every moment, and shows a new coat and appearance, as Scripture states, "All of them are like a garment which wears out, You change them like a garment and they pass away."[50] All nature turns and rotates like a wheel, and reappears in a higher guise than before; sometimes this process requires several cycles.[51]

Tell me, beloved brothers, one who has never observed the process of sowing and is told that the soul of man never dies; [if] that person is informed that when the seed of a fruit is taken and placed in the mud until it rots and disappears, that afterwards from this seed will blossom a tree, pleasant to the sight,[52] with moist leaves, beautiful flowers, sweet fruit, in which are tens of thousands of seeds similar to the one which rotted in the mud, what will he think of that? And which of these two varieties of life, the human and the botanical, will he believe in the most?

Will he not think to himself that this action of sowing of which he has been told is a fantasy of the lying heart, adorned with appealing words? Will he not rather believe in the survival of the soul? For how is it possible that the seed, after it rots and disappears, should grow like a nursling with the freshness of its youth, and increase ten-thousandfold more than it was at its start? Nevertheless, so it is.

Or shall we imagine an Italian or a Sicilian who has never seen or heard of winter, snow, or ice. If he were to come to our city in the winter and see all these wonders, with the trees as dry as bones, what would this person think? Would he not say to himself, "Here nature is indeed dead as man [dies], never to be revived"?

But is this imagined death which dominates the winter in all of nature not the cause of its life, its sleep without a spark of life? Does this not represent a [time of] rest, while [nature] gathers its energies to return in spring to its youthful vigor, when it will be seen in doubled glory? So too our deaths are only in order that we return to a renewed life brighter and more beautiful than our present existence!

This is what the verse says: "You hid Your Face"[53]—from the earth in winter, and all creatures "are frightened";[54] they lie as dead carcasses. But I say, "Gather in their spirit, and they perish," even though I see that they perish; I know that even though their spirit will be gathered, and even though "they return to their dust," that is only in order that "You will send again Your spirit," Your spirit of life, "they will be recreated and You will renew the face of the world."[55]

Observe, "God's glory will be forever";[56] quickly in that future springtime, the glory of His Kingdom will appear, the dead trees will be adorned with their youthful greenery again, and be beautified with flowers and fine fruit which will spread their sweet scent, by which the birds fly, soaring through the air in their joy, singing the beauty of the world and all therein between the branches, till "God rejoices in His creations."[57]

Therefore, if I see on one side that "he looks at the earth and it trembles,"[58] that trouble occurs to a person, or even death, that "He touches the mountains" of man's bliss "and they smoke,"[59] I will not tremble, but "I will sing to God while I live,"[60] that is, because of the life which He gave me, which He will not take from me, "I will hymn to God while I am still alive,"[61] for "I will yet live," and will not come to an end.

From Nature in General

3. However, apart from this proof that death is only imaginary from nature in general, and [that it] only brings [in its wake] a new life, we have a third proof from [nature's] individual creatures, [viz.,] that no primary element of creation can be utterly annihilated and disappear entirely.[62] Take whatever you wish, crush it, grind it up, burn it, do with it what you will, and you will not be able to destroy it entirely. If so, how could the most precious and noble thing in nature and among all the creations, that is, man's soul, [be treated less than] the most inferior of [God's creations, in that] it can be utterly annihilated?

This proof too is gloriously recorded in Holy Scripture [when] King Solomon, peace be on him, writes, "I know that all which God has made will exist forever,"[63] and will not be annihilated by nature;[64] truly, "nothing can be added to it,"[65] that is, one cannot transform a four-legged creature into a winged one, or a bird with wings into a four-legged creature[66]—rather, "from it one cannot diminish,"[67] you cannot diminish [a part of creation] from the world and annihilate it.

Why did the Creator arrange His world in this way? The reason is that "God did [this in order] that they should fear Him,"[68] not to sin against Him, not to think that the grave will be a refuge for you,"[69] and imagine that "the Holy One, blessed be He, can punish me only in this world, but when I am in Sheol I will be totally annihilated, God forbid, and there will be my refuge, that God cannot reach me to punish me there." It is for this reason that God arranged [matters] so that you will not cease to exist, in order that you know with certainty that the soul, which is the most important thing in the world, will not in the end cease to exist.

Perhaps you will ask me whence has the flame of the candle which has been put out [i.e., the soul] gone, where has the freshness [lit. "moisture"] of the garments which have been washed and dried [i.e., the body] fled, and therefore you must admit that something in nature has indeed ceased to exist and been annihilated.

To this I will reply to you: Know that the Holy One, blessed be He, gave a power to the air of heavens, called "atmosphere,"[70] which draws and combines all the moisture and warmth, or warm mists which rise from the earth, until they reach above and are formed into clouds, and from which they are emptied again onto the earth as rain, as [Scripture] writes, "A mist went up from the earth and watered the surface of the ground."[71]

This too we find in the living and eternal words of our holy Torah, in the reproof which the wise woman [of Tekoa] gave King David, peace be on him, for not wishing to forgive [his rebellious son] Absalom, [when] she said, "For we will certainly die,"[72] that is, a century hence nothing will remain here of all of us, or of all animals and plants [now living]—all will be as though they had never existed.

But will all be truly destroyed? No. Only "like water which is absorbed" into the ground, "which will not be gathered," and will not be drawn out by human hand. Nevertheless, after a year examine the place in which it flowed, and behold, the earth is dry and as though [the water] had never flowed [there]—where has it gone? It is only by human agency that it cannot be gathered, but [rather the water] has risen into the sky, and [though] much of it has sunk into the earth, of this too, [much] will rise by mists into the sky, and from there return to earth as rain. *It will not be destroyed* [emphasis added—Y.E.].

[As] the wise woman concluded her words to the king, that so much "will God bear a soul"—to uproot it from the source of life and annihilate it—"in order that no one banished will be banished [forever]," [73] that is, even a person who is truly and completely wicked, and who should be totally banished from life, in man's short-sighted opinion—nevertheless, the Holy One, blessed be He, in His great mercy will not banish him. Even one who seems banished is only banished in man's sight, but not before Him, may He be blessed. And in this is the great reproof to the king, who banished Absalom and did not wish to allow him to return; "you have done something which is neither God's way nor nature's way, for nothing may be annihilated."

As for you, my dear brother, if you wish to see the resurrection of the dead before your very eyes, observe the worm called a caterpillar (German *Raupe*), which lives but a few weeks, crawls, slithers, and eats, until a convulsion seizes it. It [then] weaves a woolly cocoon about itself, and it becomes hard within it, its housing becoming its grave. There it remains as though dead for five or six weeks—I myself have opened its cocoon during this time, and found a corrupt thing, seemingly rotten—but after the end of the time of its formation within the cocoon, it pierces its shell and comes out to the light as a new creature, with stunning, beautiful wings, as a live butterfly, joyously flitting to and fro.

So will be the end of your life as a caterpillar (German *Raupe*), O man buried, there you will form yourself for another life and from there will God redeem you, as your compassionate Father has Himself declared, "For I am God when I open your graves,"[74] and with wings of flame will you fly to the heavens above.

This is what Scripture says clearly, "If he swallows him from his place," that is, man, "denies him, [saying,] 'I did not see you,' " for all say that he is as one whom we never saw, [but] "so is his happy lot, and from his earth others will grow,"[75] in the heavenly land [to which] he will be restored, as a flowering tree to life, as [Scripture] says, "rooted in the house of God"[76]—the world-to-come. There is the root of life, and there he will flourish, but in the "courtyards of our God,"[77] that is, in this world, they will [only] "flower"[78] only as a flower which prepares the way for regeneration.

In my humble opinion, this is what our sages, may their memory be blessed, said in Berakhot (43b): One who goes out in [the month of] Nissan and sees trees budding should recite [the blessing] "Blessed are You, O God, our Lord, King of the Universe, Who did not make His world lack for anything, and created in it good creatures and good trees for humans to be beautified by them." The inclusion of animals in this blessing for trees is mystifying, even though they too appear beautiful in the spring; he should recite the blessing on trees [alone] when he sees them. Moreover, why does [the blessing] conclude [with the words] "for humans to be beautified by them"?

However, [this is to be understood as follows:] The world and its creatures stand in close relation. What occurs to one occurs to the other. In winter, not only is the world wintry, but all creatures in it suffer weakness and are sunk in stupor and cold; low spirits rule all.

But when the first rays of spring reach the earth, all are revived; all nature awakens to new, youthful life. As [Scripture] says, "New of mornings,"[79] that is, every morning new life appears in nature, and new powers arise, "great is Your faithfulness,"[80] how great are You, O God! For in the winter you loan nature worldly powers, and you pay us a doubled percentage of what You loaned her!

It is for this reason that our sages, may their memory be blessed, state in Pesahim (112b) [that] "when you see a black ox in the days of [the month of] Nissan [when he is in heat], [even if] the head of the ox is in his feedbag, climb up to the attic and throw down the ladder [behind you]," that is, leave the vicinity of the animals which are liable to harm you then in their wildness.

All creatures and humans are more fit for life than for death, for health and recovery more than for weakness and lack of strength, for joy and pleasure more than for sorrow and heartbreaking pain.

As for the Jew, he should always find ways of seeking perfection in the changes of nature, and therefore when he sees trees budding in the spring, that is, when he sees small moist blooms on the branches of trees, he should remember that man too is [like] a tree;[81] this tree too is as though destroyed, without moisture in the winter, its old age, but at winter's end it awakens to spring, more beautiful [than it was], and returns to its youthful life again, to bud with new vitality.

The [Jew] declares, "Blessed is the One Who did not cause His world to lack for anything," Who did not allow anything to be annihilated. That dying stupor which we saw in nature in winter was only a preparation for the perfection which will come after it, for the lack which we saw in winter is the very vehicle for creating new and useful creatures, which are more beautiful and stronger in heart than at the end of the harvest. And the trees too are now more beautiful than they were then, for now they return to their youthful vigor.

[Thus] one concludes [with] the essential intent of the blessing, that this was ordained by the Creator, may He be blessed, "in order that humans be beautified through them," that through this, man will consider that death too is imaginary; it will carry him to new life, and the thundercloud of death will carry him to heaven as Elijah, to be lit with the light of life before God.

Thus, we have had three strong proofs of the survival of the soul, viz., from our own experience, from nature in general, and from [God's] creatures in particular.

From the Holy One Blessed Be He

4. Why, however, can we not bring proof from the Holy One, blessed be He, Himself, our good Father in Heaven, Lord of all souls, Source of life, from "with You is the Source of life, in Your light we see our own light"?[82]

Don't you believe, O my brother, that there is one God in existence? Indeed, there is no intelligent being in all the world that does not believe this, for if not, who brought forth to light this well-designed natural order, as we see? If so, if you believe this, you must also believe in the survival of the soul.

Tell me, my friend, answer, what is God? You will answer that He is the high and exalted Essence, Soul of the world and its vital Force, Who brings all into being, is omnipresent, omniscient, of infinite wisdom, of unending goodness, of righteousness without limit, of power without bound. That all these characteristics are His, may He be blessed, is apparent to us from His actions, and no one in the world will doubt this.

Now, if we think that when a person dies, God forbid, his soul too ceases to exist, as a cloud dissipates, then the intellect which God has bestowed upon humans serves only to humble and denigrate him to a lower level than the beasts of the field. For when an animal is placed under the slaughterer's knife, it still does not know that in a moment it will cease to exist and be as though it never was. Man, from the moment of his awareness, knows that he cannot be saved from death, which he will encounter in the end; if so, when he rises and lies down,[83] this thought will torture him, that this sad state is his foreordained end.

Is it for this that God granted man the torch of intellect, that with its light he will see the fearful terror and trouble, his sunset and darkness? [If this is so,] where is [God's] goodness, may He be blessed, His wisdom and knowledge?

Moreover, we see that in the ordinary course of events, not only is a righteous man not rewarded for his righteousness, but often he suffers many troubles and evils, while the evildoer oftentimes is not only not punished, but is blissful in his evildoing and attains power. Unless we say that the righteous person's misfortunes are not [intended as] a trial [of his faith and patience] and the success of the wicked person [is not the result] of [God's] restraining His anger, where are God's omniscience and righteousness, well known to all, if reward and punishment are not deferred for the survival of the soul?

The psalmist devoted an entire chapter of Psalms to this matter. "God is my shepherd; I shall not want,"[84] that is, I am [like] small cattle which You herd in Your world, and when I believe [in this] "I shall not want," [I shall not lack] for anything in this world, for the Holy One, blessed be He, does not save anyone but one who considers himself as a beast [of the field] (Hullin 5b), but also in the next world I will lack for nothing myself.

For if "He makes me lie down in green pastures,"[85] viz., if He bestows goodness on my fleshly life, if in the pastures of life I obtain my food and drink and all my [material] needs with ease and without toil, then I will know that He has made me lie down in my pleasures; only He with His great arm "leads me by pleasant waters,"[86] and not my own abilities; [I do not claim that] my own strength won me this wealth.[87]

If "my soul goes astray,"[88] and I fall into wild ways, and am seized with failure as a fish on a hook, I know "that He leads me in right paths,"[89] I recognize His righteousness, may He be blessed. For this [misfortune has occurred] either to purify my soul, because I sinned against Him, may He be blessed, or against people, or [this misfortune] motivates me to repent of my foolishness, or [alternatively,] this [misfortune] is a test [of my faith], or [is intended] to guard me from sin. All this I am obliged to believe "for His Name's sake,"[90] in which is included all five apprehensions enumerated above, viz., that He is omnipotent, and He is omniscient, that He is the essence of wisdom, and the essence of justice, and that He is one truly beneficent Being. From all this it follows that all that occurs to me in my world must be for my [own] good.

However, "even when I walk in the valley of death,"[91] when I come to the dark valley of death, viz., when I lie on my deathbed, with my shattered vision I will venture a glance at You, my dear Father, "I will not fear"[92] darkening and annihilation—and this for three reasons.

(1) For I know that wherever I am "You are with me."[93] As my distress grows in this world, You are closer to me, and certainly when I am in danger, if I lie ill, You are closest to me, as our sages, may their memory be blessed, say: "the Divine Presence is above the bed of a person who is ill" (Nedarim 40[a]), that is, Divine Providence is greater for him.

And if so, it is most certain that for one who is in the greatest danger, that is, when body and soul are about to separate, the compassionate Father will certainly look carefully at His child who lies in pain, to restore his soul. [Thus] our sages assert (Niddah 30[94][b]) [regarding the verse] that "before Him all who descend to the Pit bow the knee"[95]—that everyone merits a vision of the Divine Presence at the moment of death in order to ease the pain of this passage, as [Scripture] says: "in the light of the King of Life,"[96] and if the Holy One, blessed be He, lavishes so much attention on him, how can it be that in the end the soul will cease to exist, like ashes strewn [before the wind]?

(2) Your staff, the royal scepter which You stretched out to me more than any other creature, inasmuch as You crowned me with the crown of intellect, by means of which I will prove that my soul will not cease with my death—will You allow the light of this pure candle shining before me only to show me the darkness that faces me and my [ultimate] failure? Where then is [His] supernal wisdom; where then is His omnipotence and His unending goodness?

(3) "Your staff,"[97] which [refers to] Your punishment of the wicked in this world as well, crushing him measure for measure, and in this way You demonstrate that it is impossible to deny that [it is] Your hand which does this in Your love of justice—if I were to think that I will expire like a cloud [which dissipates], God forbid, where is Your wondrous justice?

All these are strong proofs, as clear as a glass, "and they comfort me,"[98] calming my mind.

Therefore, even if I see that "You have set a table before me for my enemies,"[99] [that is,] if I see that You have set great tables for my enemies, and Your enemies (Your foes, O God, I hate),[100] who sing with joy over their banquets in this world, nevertheless, I consider that, for my part, "You anoint my head with oil,"[101] as though You have anointed me with the oil of kingship. For behold, in my elevated, royal nature, I will not grieve for the lack of the material pleasures that I see [my enemies] enjoy, [but] rather think that "my cup runs over,"[102] as though my cup of salvation[103] is filled to overflowing.

For I know with a certainty that "only good and kindness will pursue me all the days of my life"[104]—in this world, "and I will return[105] [to] the house of God for many long years"[106]—that is, I will return to sit in the house of God for many long years without end, and I will proceed from strength to strength.[107] I will not cease to exist nor ever be annihilated.

[5.] Behold, my brothers! We have already cited four very strong proofs regarding the survival of the soul, but our holy Torah will place seal engravings[108] holy to God[109] on all of these with its words as glowing as pearls, her breasts like towers[110] to nurture her children on milk and honey.[111]

For the heretics brazenly claim that there is no hint [of this] in our holy Torah, but come, my brothers, cast your weak eyes [on the matter] and let us search [together], for there is literally no section of the Torah which does not mention this matter, but it is visible only to those who have eyes [to see], [to those] who have the ability to see and wish to see [it].

In Genesis, when Cain murders Abel, God's voice calls out

to him, "The sound of your brother's blood cries out to Me from the earth,"[112] and demands revenge. But if Abel's soul was cut off entirely upon leaving his body, where is there sound or utterance?

In regard to Noah [Scripture] states, "One who sheds human blood—his blood will be shed."[113] "However, I will demand your blood for your souls [if you shed human blood],"[114] that is to say, I will demand this from one who kills himself. But if after death the soul dissipates like a cloud, and becomes as nothing, when will He demand [punishment] for this terrible sin [of suicide]?

In the portion of Lekh Lekha it is written that "one who is uncircumcised, ... who is not circumcised, that soul will be cut off from its people, etc."[115] If the soul ceases to exist when it issues from the body, what warning is this for one who violates the covenant [of circumcision]?

And so too in portion after portion; only seek carefully and you will find this matter [between the lines of the text].

From the Torah Itself

There are heaps and heaps of such proofs throughout Holy Scripture. "The dust shall return to the earth as it is, but the spirit will return to the Lord."[116] "How great is Your goodness which You have stored up for those who fear You."[117] "As for Your treasured ones, fill their bellies; their sons too shall be satisfied, and have something to leave over for their young. Then I, justified, will behold Your face; awake, I am filled with the vision of You."[118] "For You will not abandon me to Sheol, or let Your faithful one see the Pit. You will teach me the path of life, in Your presence is perfect joy, delights are ever in Your right hand."[119]

II. The State of the Soul After Death

After having cited these five proofs for the survival of the soul, now let us examine the state of the soul after it leaves the body, and what [part] of the righteous soul can nevertheless be annihilated after death. Before this, however, we will answer four strong questions regarding the necessity of [the penalty of] extirpation [*karet*], with the help of God.

We know that extirpation is the most terrible punishment which can be visited on a person, and affects both the soul and the body—both are annihilated entirely.

Objection to the Justice of the Penalty of Extirpation (Karet)

According to our sages, may their memory be blessed (Mo'ed Katan 28a), one who is liable to [the penalty] of extirpation will die before the age of sixty, and his minor children will likewise die. Tosafot (Shabbat 25a and Yevamot 2a) limit [this matter] of the death of minor children [to those who were] alive at the time of the transgression to cases in which [Scripture] states "they shall die childless,"[120] such as the case of one who has intercourse with a menstruant woman, and the like.

The cutting off of the soul is explained by Maimonides (Hilkhot Teshuvah, chap. 5), who writes that whoever is liable to [the penalty of] extirpation, after death his soul ceases to exist and is annihilated and becomes as naught, and that is the plain meaning of the [Scriptural] expression "that soul shall certainly be cut off,"[121] viz., that its existence in the world shall be cut off.

However, there are [several] questions to be raised regarding this matter.

(1) What punishment can affect the body, soul, and children of one who has several times transgressed a matter which brings the [penalty of] extirpation? After all, after his first terrible transgression he has already lost [any hope] of success in this world or in heaven, both his body and soul are condemned to be ground up, and what then is left to destroy? And what is the punishment of one who has passed the age of sixty when transgressing a sin whose penalty is extirpation?

(2) There is no reason to question the Torah's assertion that the seed of one who is liable to extirpation will also come to an

end, even though we see that in some cases the offspring of
people [of this sort] do not die, for it is possible that this punishment is carried out beyond human ken, for on occasion this
punishment is not exacted until the sixth or seventh generation, all according to the weight of the transgression, which is
revealed [only] to God, may He be blessed.

This matter is hidden from ordinary people, for most
people do not have records of their ancestry going back so far,
but it can be seen [by examining] the records of royal dynas-
ties, which are more available to scrutiny. On occasion a noble
or a king has three or four sons, and after several centuries the
entire family disappears, as is known to any reader of world
history. This is because extirpation is applicable even to non-
Jews. [Since] in regard to Noahides[122] [the rule is that] they are
liable to penalties not explicitly stated in the Torah so long as
their prohibition is recorded (Sanhedrin 57a), and most sins
which carry the death penalty meted out by a human court also
involve the penalty of extirpation [if a court does not punish
them], why should Noahides be less liable to this than Jews?

However, [the matter of extirpation] is difficult to understand, since we see that many people who are liable to [this pen-
alty] by reason of having had intercourse with a menstruant
woman or violated the Sabbath, or even more, consistently violated the Torah's most heinous prohibitions, and yet on occasion they live to a foolish ripe old age.[123] Can it possibly be, God
forbid, that the Torah is telling us something contrary to reality?

(3) The mishnah which states that "all Israel have a share in
the world-to-come, as [Scripture] states, 'Your people are all
righteous,'[124]"[125] is also difficult. Who is the tanna speaking of?
If he intends [all] righteous people, pious gentiles are also included, since they too have a portion in the world-to-come; the
only difference is in the size of the portion. A Jew may expect
a portion proportional to the mitzvot he performs, but he also
may lose more than [individuals] of other nations when he is

not careful to keep the mitzvot of his God. Why then [did the mishnah] specify that "all Israel have a share in the world-to-come"?

Thus you must conclude that [the mishnah] refers to wicked persons as well, as the phrase "all Israel" implies—even those who are liable to being cut off or subjected to a court-ordered execution. "A Jew who sins is still a Jew."[126] This is, however, difficult, since how is he to retain a portion in the world-to-come if his soul is annihilated? Aside from this, how can the tanna [of our mishnah] refer to the wicked when [the verse states] "Your people are all righteous"?

Response: God's Two Lights

[All this may be explained as follows:] We find [the following teaching] in a midrash (*Leviticus Rabbah* 31) on the verse "It is You Who light my lamp; God, my Lord, lights up my darkness."[127]

> Said the Holy One, blessed be He, to Israel: "My sons, My lamp is in your hands, and your lamp is in My hands. If you light My lamp, I will light yours; but if you do not light My lamp, I will not light yours."

What are these two lamps, which when we light one, the Holy One, blessed be He, lights the second?

The Cleansing of the Soul After Death
The Righteous

[The solution is contained in the verse] "The soul of man is the lamp of God, [Who] searches out all the chambers of the heart."[128] God has lit two spiritual lamps within us. One is the divine spark which invigorates the structure of the body and all it contains; this is the holy light which is itself, as it were, "the portion of God above,"[129] as [the verse states,] "He breathed into his nostrils the soul of life"—as one inflates a wineskin, as it were, when only the breath which the inflator breathes into the skin fills it.

However, since this spiritual spark is to the highest degree ethereal, while the body is altogether gross and material, to the extent that the[se] two antitheses of [man's nature] can hardly be combined, therefore God created a third element which is midway between the two. This [mediating element] is the "animal soul," or, as it is called, the "nerve spirit" (German *Nervengeist*). This is the dim candle by which soul and body are combined so that all three [elements] are wonderfully amalgamated, remaining together all through man's life so that to all appearances they form one unit. He cannot seek his essence within himself, for he will think that he himself is made up of but one element; [he thinks] that the body is the soul and the soul the body, for to his mind all constitute one element.

So it is in life, but after death each constituent separates from the other, as [Scripture] states, "and the dust returns to the earth as it was, and the spirit returns to God Who gave it."[130] The spirit mentioned [here] is the holy spark we mentioned, which was given to man by God's hand, and so, as it were, it emanates from His Godhead, may He be blessed, and thus is not subject to destruction but returns to its Source.

But the animal soul, which mediates between the soul and the body, was brought into being only [by the necessity] of combining the parts of the body, and so it is reasonable[131] that when[132] the parts of the human being are separated, this [animal] soul loses its existence. But the Holy One, blessed be He, promised us that if we keep the mitzvot of our Lord this [soul] also will not cease to exist.

Thus the two Sabbath candles hint at a world which is "all Sabbath" [i.e., the world-to-come], when both lamps will shine for us, the one corresponding to the command of "Keep [the Sabbath]," which is the holy spark which we need to keep so that its lamp will not dim, and the second lamp, corresponding to "Remember [the Sabbath],"[133] which we have to remember its status and intensify its light.

This is what the midrash says [regarding the verse,] "It is You Who lights my lamp; God my Lord lights my darkness."[134] Is there not a contradiction between the two parts of the verse, one which speaks of "my lamp," and the other of "my dark- ness"?

Rather, this is what the Holy One, blessed be He, says to man: "My lamp is in your hand," that is, the supernal spark which is My lamp, viz., the divine spark from Himself, as it were, which you can darken with your sins. But even your darkened lamp, viz., the animal soul, is in My hand. If you light My su- pernal lamp from the elevated world which I have placed within you, if you keep it from the filth of sin, then I too will light your lamp, viz., the animal spirit [i.e., soul] which is in you. I will give it continued existence so that it will continue to live even when it leaves the body, that the two of them [body and soul,] will continue forever.

In this way I interpret [the verse] "He guards all my bones, not one has been broken,"[135] [which is] difficult; to what period does it refer? If it refers to the life of a righteous person in this world, does the righteous person not wish that not only his bones be unharmed but also, if his flesh is hurt, his soul grieves [for this] as well. And if it refers to the period after death, the righteous one is indifferent [yishveh] to the breaking of one of his bones, as in truth we hold that one may hand over the bones of a dead person to be broken (and as to [the rule] prohibiting [such an action in] Yoreh De'ah 403, that is only when [one does so] for no reason).

It seems to me, however, that [all] this refers to the future reward of the righteous, and the word etzem, which the verse employs, does not refer to the "bone" but rather has the mean- ing of the word in the verse "and like the essence of the heav- ens for purity."[136] That is, that the Holy One, blessed be He, guards all the essences of a righteous person, viz., all the grada- tions of his soul, *nefesh, ru'ah, neshamah, hayah, yehidah.*[137] Not one part of his soul will go to perdition, but "not one will be broken," viz., not one will "be broken" after death. [This refers] to the holy and elevated spark of that true divine spark, as it were, which cannot cease to exist.

Ordinary People

However, all this refers to a totally righteous person, since for such a person the soul separates into its constituent elements upon death, and only the *havla de-garma* (called *Knochengeist* ["bone-spirit" in German])[138] remains attached to the bones. Even so, all the elements of the soul remain in loose contact, especially at the time of the "birth" of the new moon, the fifteenth of the month, and the anniversary of the deceased person's death (*yahrzeit*). It is therefore appropriate to visit the graves of one's ancestors at these times, for then the soul flies near to and around the grave and the skeleton.[139]

However, it is impossible for a sinful soul to be separated into its constituent elements immediately after death, and for the spirit to return to God, as noted above, since the holy spark has acquired several black marks from sins committed on the individual's journey through this world. Now, after death, when the soul stands alone, [these marks] cannot be cleansed, since the soul's lofty nature forbids its being subject to the necessities of time.[140]

Therefore, after the soul's exit [from the body], two of its constituent elements [i.e., the animal soul and the soul proper] remain linked together, for by their union the aforementioned spark is [again] subject to time, as in its earthly life. In this way it becomes open to receiving its twelve-month-long punishment, more or less, according to the number of its sins, in order that it be well purified. After this the [two constituent elements] once again sit before God, to receive their [proper] reward for their good deeds. (It is for this reason that the tanna [of Sanhedrin 10:1] states that "*all* [Israel will have a portion in the world-to-come]," including the sinner whose punishment is in

Gehenna, for he too is readied for the [God's] spiritual meal after his term of punishment.)

This, in my humble opinion, is the intent of our rabbis in Sanhedrin (91a) [in regard to the conversation of Antoninus and Rabbi]. Antoninus asked Rabbi [how it was that] the body and the soul could acquit themselves of condemnation [for sins committed], for either one alone cannot commit a sin. Rabbi answered with the well-known parable of the cripple and the blind man; so too the Holy One, blessed be He, combines body and soul together and judges them as one entity.

The intent is that it is not the body itself which recombines with the soul, for we see that the body rests, corrupt and inanimate, in the grave, as [in the case of] the well-known[141] mummies (German *Mumien*), which have been well-known[142] these thousands of years. Can it be imagined that Titus was correct in ordering that "[his body] be burnt in fire and its ashes scattered over the seven seas so that the Jewish God not find him [and judge him]"?[143]

[The statement] that He reinvests the body with the soul [refers] to the strength of the body, that is, the animal soul that we spoke of. This is [to be compared] to the blind man who cannot choose between what is good and bad for him; moreover, his sightlessness deprives him of full satisfaction of his earthly needs (as in Yoma 74b), and as our sages have explained, "No one dies with half his wants satisfied."[144]

The cripple [of the parable] is thus the supernal soul, which has no power to act in this world if it is not borne by the body's blind strength; only the supernal soul can show [the body] the way to go, for it is [to the body] as the captain of a vessel [to the vessel]. These two powers are recombined after their separation from the body so that they be purified of their blemishes.

This is the reason for the [various periods of mourning such as] *shivah*,[145] the thirty-day period, and the twelve months that children mourn their parents. "For there is no man [perfectly] righteous in this world who does good and does not sin."[146] It is for this reason that this secret was imparted to us, for the process of purification [can proceed that] slowly.

Therefore, the children [of the deceased], or their representatives, attempt to increase their performance of mitzvot during this period of purification, or to study for the sake [of their parents' souls]. For since the parents brought the children into this world, and raised and guided them to Torah and fear of God, which motivate the children to perform the mitzvot they do, the [principle] that "one who causes [another] to do a mitzvah is greater than the one who does it" (Bava Batra 9a) [applies], and the Holy One, blessed be He, considers the mitzvot performed [by the children] as though the parents had done them.

This all applies to an ordinary person who sins [only] occasionally, but [not to] one who transgresses [a mitzvah] which involves being cut off. [The latter] is annihilated, [since] his animal soul ceases to exist after its exit [from the body], like a branch cut off from a tree, [and thus] has no life.

On the Penalty of Extirpation

This is the [meaning] of the verse, "that soul shall surely be cut off,"[147] viz., the animal [soul], "its sin is within it,"[148] for alone it cannot survive forever, since it is [by nature] combined [with the supernal soul].

The supernal soul cannot be purified without having been made subject to time. Thus when [the two souls] depart from the body they remain together and proceed together until the[ir] holy spark is well cleansed and purified. After the days of cleansing are ended,[149] the animal soul is obliterated as a vessel which no longer has any use. The holy spark itself returns to shine in the Light of Life, returns to the Divine Camp.

Thus our sages say (Rosh Hashanah 17[a]) that "the bodies of those liable to [the penalty of] being cut off[150] cease to exist," that is, the body's strength, its animal power, ceases, and "their souls are burnt up," that is, they are made incandescent like iron in the forge, and "the spirit," that is, the spirit of God, sprinkles their ashes under the feet of the righteous in the Garden of Eden.

Observe this precious image presented to us by our sages, who compared that part of the soul which can be brought to an end to a [piece of] wood which can be burnt up, for though much of the wood can be destroyed, its ashes cannot. So too the soul after it has been made incandescent in the forge and parts of it have been destroyed, nevertheless the spirit of the Living God insufflates the Divine part of it, to place it on the lowest rung of [those allocated to] the righteous who receive the reward of their efforts. This "daughter who returns to her father's house" [after divorce, i.e., the soul of one liable to being cut off] and thus eats shameful bread [provided by her father rather than her husband], is nevertheless not repulsed altogether,[151] for she is a princess.

In this way the first question we asked can be answered, how one who is liable to several penalties of being cut off can be punished. According to our explanation, the time of his purification and pain is proportional to the number of penalties he has incurred, until [finally] the holy spark is [completely] purified. On occasion even many hundreds of years may not suffice to accomplish this purification, as we find in the *Shelah* [i. e. the *Shenei Luhot ha-Berit* of R. Isaiah Horowitz], who [in a dream] saw a man into whom a sinning spirit entered,[152] and [this sinning spirit] was of one of the early [Israelites] who had raised a stone to stone the prophet Zechariah, peace be on him, in the [First] Temple—more than fifteen hundred years later![153]

If this is so, our second question, too, is answered. We asked how it is that we often see people who have several times incurred [the penalty of] being cut off, yet live to a ripe old age. Since it is impossible to fulfill the penalty of being cut off in his bodily existence, [this person] is "paid off" by being punished in the next world. The same [rule holds] for one who should have died before his time, when on occasion it is impossible for his death to occur except miraculously.

[This miraculous intervention is difficult.] For the Holy One, blessed be He, sealed His world with the royal seal, the seal of nature, which does not change easily (see my commentary in Seder Nashim 154a).[154] Thus, happy is one who is liable to the penalty of being cut off who receives the punishment set for him in this world, for if he prevents this punishment from affecting him, viz., he guards his health carefully [and] when he becomes but slightly ill he quickly calls an expert doctor who prescribes drugs for him, which cure him—do you think that God will change the [course of] nature for this fool who has sinned (as we see in Avodah Zarah 55[a])?

But [though] "the goats run and the shepherd limps, the accounting comes [in the end, in any case] at the sheepfold" (as in Shabbat 32a), for had he received his punishment of shortened lifespan in this world, his punishment and purifying sufferings would have been better for him in this measure, and happy would he have been!

But woe to him who prevents [his] Creator, may He be blessed, from settling his account in a natural way! Instead of receiving a passing punishment—a shortened lifespan—in this world, the sinner receives an eternal one in the world-to-come. According to this calculation, his punishment and purifying sufferings, [intended] to cleanse thoroughly the holy spark, are long and hard in the next world, before the animal soul, this lower lamp, is extinguished by the penalty of being cut off.

Thus the third question, too, is answered. The mishnah refers to "all Israel," even the wicked, those who are liable to being cut off and to execution by the order of an earthly court, so long as he bears the title "Israel."[155] He has a portion in the world-to-come inasmuch as he may receive his reward in the next world, that is, the holy spark which is capable of [continued] existence [even for the wicked], for whatever befalls, this [part of the soul] will continue to exist, as explained above.

However, among the nations of the world only the righteous and pious have a portion in the world-to-come, but their wicked ones, "God's enemies, will be consumed like meadow grass consumed in smoke,"[156] for only Israel has the holy spark which we mentioned, and it is for this reason that they were commanded mitzvot and laws of the Torah which will perfect this holy spark in a wondrous way (as will be explained, with the help of God, in the sixth chapter of Avot, p. 264b).

And thus [the mishnah of Sanhedrin 10:1, mentioned above] concludes with "and Your people are all righteous," that is, each one of them in general, in the two parts of his soul, is perfect; they have not transgressed in a way which would open them to the penalty of being cut off. Thus, "they will inherit the land forever," that is, along with the Eternal they will have a material world as well, and arise with the resurrection of the body, for all will remain in existence, the animal and spiritual souls. And so, at the time of the resurrection of the dead, the whole society [of Israel] may be reconstituted as before.

However, one who has no merit but that of [being] "the planting of My hand," in that "I created him, shaped and formed him,"[157] at least "to glory in My works," [his] animal soul ceases to exist and is cut off, and he does not arise again with the resurrection of the dead, since he lacks an essential element of the elements necessary for bodily life. If he receives another animal soul, he will not then recognize himself! For this strange combination will form a new creature altogether.

In any case, however, the holy spark within him, which is His handiwork, will return, after its purification and cleansing, to shine in the Light of God, since it is His handiwork, so to speak, as [Scripture] states, "and [as for] the souls, I made [them]"[158]—to glory in.

Thus, a wicked person of this sort also has a portion in the world-to-come, to shine with the Light of Life.

III. The Resurrection of the Dead and the Nature of Life After Resurrection

However, the belief that the body will return to life is very difficult for man to comprehend, not because of its supernatural nature, for, after all, the Holy One, blessed be He, says, "Is anything impossible for Me? says God,"[159] "Is God's ability limited?"[160] and as our sages noted, "[If] that which never was has been [brought into being], certainly something which has [already] existed will come into being!"[161]

Our wonder is, rather, at the question of the purpose of this resurrection, since we consider our earthly life of such great worth that we consider it the ultimate aim [of existence].

We wish to have a description of that new life, to know how it will be; will we then eat and drink and live as now, as Rabbenu Saadiah [Gaon] and other gaonim wrote? [Their assertion that] we will not [again] die [thereafter] is against our understanding, for [how can this be], since we will have a body similar to the one we have now? Even if we live a thousand years, even if we have a body strong as iron, in the end the end of man is to die, in the end time will grind us up.

If so, let us have neither death nor resurrection (lit. "the absence of a *heh* and a *vav* is surprising");[162] shall he not live nor die again? Does the Holy One, blessed be He, perform miracles for no reason, especially a great miracle like this, that [humans] will return to life after ceasing to exist, in order to die once more? Moreover, is not one hour of satisfaction in the next world, to imbibe the light of the Divine Presence, worth more than all the life of this world?[163]

Again, if we hold with those gaonim who disagree with R. Saadiah, and are of the opinion that we will die after the resurrection, this will not make contemplation [of this matter] any easier, for [the Talmud] in Mo'ed Katan 28a [reports the following incident]. Rava was shown R. Seorim after his decease, and he asked him, "Did the Master have any pain in dying?" And [the latter] replied, "[Only] as one removes a hair from milk, but nevertheless, if the Holy One, blessed be He, ordered that I return to this world as I was, I would not want to." For though the pain of death is not as it is imagined, since it is forgotten [by the soul] after death (and as the famous Dr. Hufeland [reports] in his precious book *Makrobiotik*, pt. II, p. 49–50),[164] nevertheless the frightfulness of death is greater than it is in actuality.

Undoubtedly, such is the thought of every human soul after death, that it does not wish to return to this dreamworld only to die once again. If so, what is the benefit of resurrection, and [thus] what punishment is it [when the Talmud declares] that usurers and similar people will not rise at the resurrection of the dead?

The Nature of His Principle of Faith

Nevertheless, despite the many problems which we have raised [regarding this tenet of our faith], every Jew who denies it is considered abominable according to the faith of our holy Torah, [and] of abysmally low degree; as Maimonides declares at the beginning of [his commentary] on Helek,[165] whoever denies this principle is a heretic and Epicurean, and has no portion in the world-to-come.

And so it is stated in the mishnah, "These have no portion in the world-to-come: whoever declares that there is no [hint of] the resurrection of the dead in the Torah." And Rashi writes [in his comments] there[on] that even one who believes in this principle, but does not believe that it can be proven from the Torah, is in the category of Epicurean.

The [author of the commentary] *Be'er Sheva* writes there that [this comment] is the result of a student error recorded on the margin of Rashi's commentary, for what difference does it make whether one declares the verses the Talmud brings in support [of this principle] as merely an *asmakhta*,[166] if he [nevertheless] believes in the principle? So too did Maimonides write in the third chapter of [*Hilkhot*] *Teshuvah*, that only one who denies the principle altogether is a heretic and has no portion in the world-to-come.

It seems that Rashi did understand the mishnah in [the way set forth above], since [the mishnah] states "from the Torah." [Nevertheless,] it seems (in my humble opinion) that the intent of this mishnah is that only one who declares that it can be proven that the Torah holds the reverse, [i.e., that there will be no resurrection,] and thus that there is no obligation to believe in it—he is in the category of Epicurean.

It is possible to reconcile Rashi's words [with this view]. He means to state that though whoever has eyes can see that the verses which the Talmud cites [in support of this principle] are only *asmakhtot*, there are several verses which speak of this matter explicitly, such as "I will put to death and bring to life,"[167] "I have smitten and I will heal,"[168] "Your dead will live and carcasses will rise,"[169] "and many of those who sleep in the dust will awake, these to eternal life,"[170] "And the angel called to Daniel, etc., and you will arise to your fate at the End of Days."[171] [Certainly,] one who wishes to remain stubborn and declare that all these verses are only metaphorical is in the category of one who distorts the Torah and has no portion in the world-to-come.

Be that as it may, our obligation is to root this belief strongly in our hearts, [so as] not to lose our [portion] in the world-to-come, which we have acquired with great exertion. For how difficult it is for us and all Israel to obtain this great bliss, and how easy it is to lose!

Proofs for the Principle of the Resurrection of the Dead and the Trustworthiness of the Torah

Therefore, I thought to satisfy Your Excellency[172] by bringing [certain] proofs as "firm as a cast mirror"[173] for this precious principle of faith. These proofs will be of three types, according to the mnemonic "for in Me is desire" [*heshek*], viz., [from] our senses (*hush*), our intellect (*sekhel*), and our Tradition (*kabbalah*), as preachers say. With these three types of proof we will be able to destroy every vestige of doubt in every weak heart.

Would that we could do this for every mitzvah of our holy Torah! As [Scripture] states, "Let me understand and I will keep Your Torah, I will keep [it] with all [my] heart,"[174] for when we understand the reason for every mitzvah, our hearts will not be torn within us. Therefore, listen to me, my beloved children, for my threshings,[175] [my well-considered thoughts,] which God has granted me, I will present to you today. Listen well, my dear friends, that you not miss one word, for all your bliss in this and the next [world] depends on it.

First we will research two things, (1) what has been, and (2) what will be. We will prove future [events] from past [ones], and even though it is forbidden for us to inquire into "what is before and what is behind," as is stated at the beginning of the first chapter of [Tractate] Hagigah, this refers to matters which go beyond those which our sages, may their memory be blessed, established for us, but we may peer through the recessed and latticed windows[176] which our Masters opened for us, as [these principles] have been handed down generation after generation, and bring strong proofs for their holy words, whose waters we drink. Likewise, [we may bring proof] from natural scientists, for it is permissible to learn from them, for God's spirit speaks in them, for all their words are true and just.

Worlds Before Our Own

[The Talmud states] in Sanhedrin 97[a][177]: "The School of Abaye[178] taught: 'Six thousand years is the [duration of the] world, with one [thousand years of] desolation.' [Furthermore,] it was taught: 'Just as the Sabbatical year cancels [debts] once in seven years, so [too] the world [has its Sabbatical] millennium once in seven thousand years.'" [The same idea is found] at the end of Tractate Tamid: "On the Sabbath [the Levites would sing] the Psalm for the Sabbath Day [Psalm 92], for a day that is all Sabbatical, rest for all time." This is the secret of all that shall be.

However, our sages, may their memory be blessed, have revealed to us, with their precious words, the secret of all that has come to pass, to shed [a little] light [on these matters as though] through the eye of a fine needle.[179]

As [it is stated in] *Genesis Rabbah*,[180] " 'It was evening and it was morning,'[181] ([thus raising] the difficulty that since the sun had not yet been created, how could there be morning and evening?). Said R. Abbahu: 'From here [we learn] that the dimension of time existed before this, etc. This teaches that the Holy One, blessed be He, created worlds and destroyed them, saying, "This satisfied Me, this does not satisfy Me." ' "

In order to perceive the matter more completely,[182] Rabbenu Bahya has revealed to us an esoteric teaching in the name of the Kabbalists[, in his commentary on] the *sidrah* of Behar, on the verse "the land shall have rest, a Sabbath to God."[183] This hints at a wondrous secret, that the world will be built up and destroyed seven times, corresponding to the seven Sabbatical years in the Jubilee—making forty-nine thousand years [in all].

And in each of these Sabbatical periods, he continues, the world is in a greater state of perfection than the preceding, so that in the end all the holy sparks that were bestowed on material beings at the beginning of creation by the Holy One, blessed be He, in order that they themselves perfect themselves, will return to the First Cause, blessed be He, in the highest state of perfection possible, as is His will, may He be blessed. This is the ultimate purpose of the creation of the world; such is the content of his words there.

Nahmanides too hints somewhat at this [doctrine], in [his comments] on the verse "which God had created to do,"[184] as does Ibn Ezra on the verse "all the days of the earth still,"[185] and Recanati on the *sidrah* of Behar, where he wrote that several mitzvot hint at this doctrine. We have seen that the number seven recurs often in several of the mitzvot, [such as] seven days of the week, seven days of Passover, seven days of Sukkot, seven days of menstrual impurity, seven days of menstrual purification, seven days before circumcision, seven days of mourning, seven days of feasting [for a wedding], seven Sabbatical years in a Jubilee, the seven branches of the menorah, seven sprinklings [of blood] on the Day of Atonement, and many more.

Those privy to the secrets of the Torah whisper that the seven cycles of the world correspond to the seven days of creation, each one of which was a preparation for the day following, as we may see from the story of creation when we examine it carefully, that each cycle is a preparation for the following cycle, and that each cycle is more highly perfected than the one before.

God's secret is [given] to those who fear Him;[186] [the Kabbalists know] that we are [now] in the fourth cycle, which corresponds to the fourth day of creation, in which the Holy One, blessed be He, set the lights in the sky. [It is for this reason] that the light of Torah [can be compared to] a sun, the greater light, lighting [the earth] from one end to the other. Though, due to our great sins, the honor of the nation has greatly declined, our holy Torah stands as a clear sun in the middle of the horizon, so that all nations, even those, as, for example, the Christians and Moslems, who feel themselves unobliged to keep the mitzvot, exalt and honor the holy Torah and recognize its divinity. [The Torah] in its honor and strength is like a sun shining its rays on all the world's inhabitants.

[Moreover, just as during creation] two lights [were fashioned], the greater light to rule the day, [corresponding to the Torah, as noted above,] and the lesser light, corresponding to man's intellect, which rules this world. This too will be greatly exalted in this cycle, and in coming times will be exalted to an extent [now] inconceivable by the human intellect.

Aside from what has been revealed to us secretly from "hand to hand" regarding [these cycles of] destruction and renewal, this matter has been well explained in [various] verses. "Broken, shattered is the earth, [crumbling, crumbled is the earth,] tottering, dislodged is the earth";[187] "the moon will be shamed and the sun will be abashed";[188] "the heaven will be rolled up like a scroll, and all their hosts will wear away";[189] "the heavens will wear away like the earth, and the earth will be worn-out like a garment";[190] "Behold, I will create a new heaven and a new earth."[191]

It is apparent from all this that the world will be renewed after it is made desolate. The [Biblical] expressions which seem to contradict this—"the world stands forever,"[192] "He established them forever"[193]—are merely figurative expressions denoting a great length of time. Likewise, "he shall serve him forever,"[194] [i.e., until the Jubilee], "you shall keep them as slaves forever,"[195] anyone will judge that the verse wishes only to denote a long period.

Geological and Paleontological Discoveries

Now, my dear friends, see how firm is the basis upon which our holy Torah rests, for this secret was revealed to our ancestors and teachers, and they revealed it hundreds of years ago, and now in our time we find this again most clearly visible to our eyes in nature.

The spirit in man which yearns, which desires to uncover all hidden matters, to search out like a mole the innards of the earth in the high mountains—the Pyrenees and the Carpathians, the Cordilleras in America, the Himalayas on the border of China—discovering that these [mountains] were formed by gigantic layers of rock which lie helter-skelter on one another with great and terrible force, hanging clifflike one on the other by a hairsbreadth, to the point at which it is impossible to imagine that this could come to pass except by a world-overturning revolution which once occurred by His hand, may He be blessed, Who reproves the earth and turns it over in a moment.

Not satisfied with this, they dug several hundreds of fathoms (German *Klafter*) into the deeps of the earth and its innards, deep into the mines (German *Bergwerk*) of the earth. They found four layers of earth, each above the other, each [made up of] a different sort of mineral, and between these layers [they found] fossils which indicate that the earth has been overturned and changed its surface four times.

The creatures found between these layers are arranged in such a way that those which lie farthest from the surface are fashioned in a larger measure than those which lie in the next layer, and so too those which lie in the second layer are larger than those which are to be found in the upper, most recent, layer. [Moreover,] the [diminution] in size [corresponds] to a

greater [degree of] perfection in the structures of the creatures
found in the upper layers [as compared to those] in the lower
layers.

Natural scientists also write that evidence exists that the
earth received a terrible blow [moving] from the southwest to
the northeast, and that by this blow the earth was blasted and
made desolate.

Likewise, in the year 1807,[196] according to their reckoning,
they found in Siberia, in the northern part of the earth, under
the terrible ice which is ever-present there, a great elephant
three or four times the size of those found today, and whose
skeleton now stands in the Zoological Museum in Petersburg.

[Moreover,] inasmuch as elephants cannot live in the extreme cold which dominates that region, [this carcass] indicates
that by the blow which the earth received and by which it was
blasted and disordered, this elephant, which once lived in a
warm climate that could support elephant life, was carried [to
its current location] by the mighty waves, or that at one time
the climate there was warm enough to support such animals.

So too they have found in the depths of the highest mountains on earth, creatures of the sea which have fossilized and
become stone; one natural scientist, Cuvier by name,[197] writes
that of every seventy-eight species of creature which are found
in the bowels of the earth, forty-eight of them no longer exist
in our modern world.

We already know of the bones of a giant creature found in
the depths of the earth around the city of Baltimore in America,
whose length is 17 feet, and whose height from the soles of its
forelegs to its shoulders is 11 feet, and from its hindlegs to its
back is 9 feet. Bones of this creature have been found in Eu-
rope too, and in the Harz Mountains, scattered all around. This
species has been named a mammoth.

They have also found fossilized remnants of a creature they
call iguanodon,[198] whose height was 15 feet and whose length
was as much as 90 feet; from the character of its limbs scientists
have judged that it ate only grass. There is yet another species

of animal called a megalosaurus, which was only a little smaller than the iguanodon, but which was a hunter and carnivorous.

From all this it is clear that the teaching of the Kabbalists, hundreds of years old, that the world has been destroyed and renewed over and over again [as many as] four times, each time in a more perfect form, is shown in our own times to be just and true.

The First Chapter of Genesis

Can you believe, my brothers, that this wonderful secret was clearly recorded in the first *parashah* of our Holy Torah, in which [is contained] all [knowledge], and which is the source of all life.[199]

(Observe well that between the folds of the beginning of the Torah, [where it] states, "In the beginning God created the heavens and the earth"—if the heavens are one element, viz., the fine gas called ether, as our sages, may their memory be blessed, state: "[The word] *shammayim* is an acronym for *esh* [fire] and *mayyim* [water], this teaches that the Holy One, blessed be He, took fire and water and mixed them together."[200] Truly, the upper air is made up of warm vapor, but the *raki'a* [firmament] is made up of the lower air, called atmosphere, made for breath, and which extends seven or eight parasangs from the earth.)

At any rate, the fact that the Torah mentions the command of the Holy One, blessed be He, "let there be an expanse [*raki'a*]," but does not record a similar command for the creation of the heavens, is difficult. And if you wish to suggest that [the *raki'a*] was created out of nothing, and so there would have been nothing to which the command could have been issued, we must still inquire as to why the creation of the four elements of earth, air, fire, and water is not mentioned.

Moreover, [the second verse of Genesis,] "the earth was empty and desolate," is altogether superfluous, for who does not know that before the Holy One, blessed be He, fashioned all the creations of this world, light did not yet exist either, [and] it is therefore obvious that all was emptiness, desolation, and darkness?

Again, it is written that "the spirit of God hovered upon the face of the waters,"[201] and yet this verse has no [clear] meaning at all. Rashi explains that [it refers to] the Glory Throne [of God] hovering [above the waters], [a remark] which itself requires explanation!

However, it would seem that here our holy Torah has revealed to us a little[202] of the wonderful secret which we mentioned [above], that this world is not in its first cycle, but that the four elements were actually created in the early cycles, and therefore are not mentioned in the [account of the] creation of the current [cycle].

That is why the Torah informs us "at the beginning," that is, at the beginning of all beginnings, "God created the heavens"— that is, the ether, which fills all three-dimensional space [*halal ha-'olam ha-nir'eh*], "and the earth"—that is, the globe of the earth. [And] after that the Torah skips over the happenings which took place in that primeval world, which do not concern us at all in our current existence.

Rather, [the Torah] tells us that "the earth was empty and desolate, etc.," that is, that emptiness and desolation were created anew, as is stated in the Targum of Jonathan ben Uziel, "the earth was empty and desolate of any humans." The intent [of the verse] is not that it was made totally desolate and emptied of existence entirely, but rather that through the Supernal Will, may He be blessed, [the earth] received a blow [as] from a "stormy wind accomplishing His word,"[203] and the primeval order of creation became a confused mixture of fire and water, and darkness came into existence above the deep.

Again, [the verse states,] "The spirit of God hovered upon the surface of the water." This [refers] to the spirit which gives life to all [living things], which is mentioned in Ezekiel 37, as [Scripture] states: "Come from the four winds, O spirit, and blow into these slain";[204] it is this same spirit which is mentioned in this connection after the Flood has passed, as [Scripture] states, "the Lord caused a wind to pass over the earth and the waters subsided";[205] [and] it is this spirit which is mentioned in connection with the creation of Adam, as is stated, "He breathed into his nostrils the spirit of life."[206] This is the spirit which is mentioned here too, viz., that the spirit of life began to hover and weave itself on the surface of the waters which covered the earth.

That is what our sages, may their memory be blessed, meant by "the Glory Throne," viz., the spirit which gives life to all [living things]. [It is that which] is called the Glory Throne, for through it one sees the glory of the King of Kings, the Holy One, blessed be He, Who is the animating force of nature, for nature is His Heavenly Throne, may He be blessed, [which] began to hover over the surface of the waters as a dove hovers over her nest, viz., to bring out its chicks.

The Torah now begins to recount the order of the current [cycle] of creation, in which each day was a preparation for the next, as explained above, as each primitive earthly cycle was a preparation for the next cycle which followed it. So too in each cycle the work of each day was a preparation for the day following. [The explanation] of these matters is lengthy, and we must now be concise, without digressing from our main subject.

Nevertheless, my dear brothers, observe the greatness and wondrous loftiness of the Torah, note the large [letter] *bet* with which the Torah opens, and scrutinize the four "crowns"[207] on that *bet*. The Kabbalists have a tradition that these four crowns hint that [the creation of] the world and all its hosts [as described therein] is the fourth [in order], and that the [letter] *bet* [which in gematria is equivalent to the number two] informs us that the crowning glory of creation, the human intellect, is here for the second time.

Early Man

In my humble opinion, those humans who lived in the primordial world, known as "pre-Adamites" in the vernacular, that is, the humans who lived in the world before the creation of Adam of the current [cycle of creation], are identical to the 974 generations mentioned in Shabbat (88[b]) and Hagigah (14[a]), who were fashioned before the current cycle of creation.

Make the following calculation: According to the words of our sages, may their memory be blessed, [this] is derived from [the verse] "He commanded a Word for a thousand genera- tions,"[208] that the Torah was fit to be given at the end of a thou- sand of these early generations, viz., at the beginning of the cur- rent cycle of creation, which was created with greater perfec- tion in intellect and character traits than the previous [one].

Now, in my humble opinion, each "generation" [of which our sages spoke] consisted of [a period] of seven years, since every seven years the world changes, as we noted above.[209] Thus the seven thousand years of the previous cycle['s existence] are the thousand generations which our sages, may their memory be blessed, mentioned. They [thus] have informed us that after the generations of the earlier [cycle] were banished from the world like thorns in the vineyard of the God of Hosts, and the world was [re]created in a more perfect fashion, it was fitting that the Torah be given to the Adam of this cycle, for the world had matured to that point.

However, since the previous world had behaved egre- giously, it was relegated to a fold in time of no consequence, and died when twenty-six [of the thousand] generations were yet to come; that is, at the end of the 974 generations which our sages, may their memory be blessed, mentioned, as noted above, according to the equation of seven years per generation, the destruction of that world [occurred] in the year 6818 from the beginning of that creation.

The twenty-six generations which were lacking in the pre- vious cycle were completed [during the period] between Adam and our Teacher Moses, viz., the ten generations from Adam to Noah, the ten from Noah to Abraham, six generations from Abraham to our Teacher Moses, when the world matured and was purified to the point of being fit for the giving of the To- rah.

This is what the verse says, "From world to world You are God,"[210] and [likewise] "Blessed is God, Lord of Israel, from world to world,"[211] for the Holy One, blessed be He, in His great mercy, in order that no one should be banished [forever], [arranges matters] so that all the holy sparks which have been given off by His Godhead, may He be blessed, in the primordial world should, by means of their free will, perfect themselves. However, since the inhabitants of the earth [of the earlier cycle] acted egregiously, and formed 974 corrupt generations which were banished from the world, He, in His great mercy, brings them back to this current, most perfect, cycle [of creation] so that it will be easier for them to perfect themselves than before, according to His Will, may He be blessed. This is what the verse mentioned above implies: "From world to world You are God," Your providence and mercy, as a Father for His children, will accompany us from world to world, constantly directing us in paths of justice.[212]

And so too it is written, "For this is God, our Lord, He directs us forever after [on] worlds,"[213] that is, as a father who wishes to accustom his young son to walk alone, and so stands him up in front of him at a short distance (viz., the time of one cycle of creation] and circles him with his arms so that if he starts to fall he will fall into his arms and [the father] will then straighten him up at this short distance as before. So will You direct us from world to world, and perfect us in each one of them, again less and less than at first, so that in the end we will draw near to You.

Our Future Intellectual Attainments

Now, my brothers, windows to the greater light have opened for us regarding this principle of faith that we have already been here, all of us, in the primordial world from which we disappeared; we may be assured by several proofs that we have come again to [this world] in the garb of a new body, more perfect than before, and again there will come a time, after we have completed our assigned tasks in this world and disappear from all eyes with our deaths, that the world will again be [re]created after the present cycle, that we will return again to be seen in the world, yet more perfect than now, as it is written, "They will sprout up in towns like the grass of the land,"[214] and so [too] it states, "The path of the righteous is like radiant light,"[215] which encircles the world again and again, "shines more brightly until the day is established"[216]— at the end of the seventh cycle, the Great Jubilee, when all the holy sparks will return to the First Cause, may He be blessed, in great perfection. This is the purpose of all creation, and this is why the verse says "until the day is established," for that is the great and terrible day which the last of the prophets mentioned at the end of his prophecy.[217]

If now, in this world, our intellects have not sufficiently matured for us to understand the secrets of the Torah's laws properly, and from several points of view we can only speculate in dark hypotheses that we have already been here, in the future world, however, this belief, [which is] our refuge, will then be clear to us with great clarity. [This is] especially [so in light of the fact that we see] in the current cycle, with greater intellectual perfection than in the previous world, that each person knows and feels what is fitting for him to do in regard to his obligations to his fellow, and understands well his natural obligations.[218] In time to come, in the future world, his eyes will be as bright as the two lights [of creation],[219] and with them will all the secrets of the earth be revealed, and all the laws of the Torah in regard to obligations and prohibitions, what he must correct and what he has corrupted in himself by means of all these. This secret is promised him. In that coming world we will be able to remind ourselves that we have already been here [in a previous life] and what we have done, etc. This is [the true significance of] the belief in the resurrection of the dead.

In my humble opinion, this is [the purport] of the Kaddish we recite after the burial, after we have hidden away the body in the secret bowels of earth, in order that those who see all this will not despair of the resurrection of the body to life, and so too to strengthen the hearts of Israel which believe in the resurrection of the dead. This is why the mourners rise to recite aloud, "May His Great Name be magnified and sanctified."

Behold, these two words, "great" and "holy," are antonyms, for "great" refers to a matter which spreads and widens until even those who are dim of sight can see [it], but the word "holy," contrariwise, refers to a matter which is set apart and hidden from all eyes.

However, according to the religion of our holy Torah and our precious faith, we must believe that the Holy One, blessed be He, has two characteristics: (1) He is high and exalted, holy and supernal, beyond the perception of any creation. (2) Though He is high and exalted and holy, He is providentially to be found in all our activities, and in all the activities of the world and of the creatures, even the lowliest, for according to His exaltedness is His humility, as is written, "For God is high and sees the humble, and perceives from afar."[220]

Though we are obligated to believe this, we cannot perceive it clearly in this world. For though we know the intensity of His holiness and hiddenness, may He be blessed, we [also] know well that "no one can see Me and live."[221] His reality is with us in all our activities, however, and all the happenstances of a person's life [occur] only through Him, may He be blessed; as our sages, may their memory be blessed, have stated, "all is in the hands of heaven [but the fear of heaven],"[222] this we may not perceive with our limited intellect, but we can [merely] believe it.

However, in this way there is a [spiritual] danger to every sinner who thinks that if he does not strive for his own [material] betterment he will not be able to achieve it, and it seems to him that whatever he achieves in this world he has accomplished by his own efforts.[223] And he therefore pursues every bodily pleasure and profit, whether in a forbidden or a permitted manner.

(9) Therefore, all mortals of whatever degree will praise the Name of God and call one to the other,[224] "Holy, holy, holy,"

that is, separate and hidden is He, blessed be He; in all three known worlds, the terrestrial, the heavenly, and the realm of angels, all ask one another "Where is the place of His Glory?"[225] for they cannot perceive His essence, may He be blessed; nevertheless, the wonder is that "the whole earth is full of His Glory."[226] [The meaning of this is] that despite His exaltedness and hiddenness, all believe that His Providence fills all the spaces of the material and spiritual worlds.

And so it is written, "Behold, this one stands behind our walls"[227]—in hidden form, even so He peers through the windows, viz., if windows of bliss are opened for us, He is the one who keeps an eye upon us, but He also "peers through the lattice,"[228] when [His] creations are plunged in the darkness of trouble, He peers at them, looking through a narrow crack in the wall, observing [them] but unseen [Himself]; so too He, may He be blessed, watches over humankind with a compassionate eye to mitigate [its] troubles and to alleviate its bitterness as much as possible—but humans do not see Him, and think that God does not look upon us at all.

Revelation After Revelation

But in the world after the resurrection of the dead His Glory will be revealed, and eye to eye all flesh will see[229] and apprehend His Godhead, may He be blessed—so much so that our sages, may their memory be blessed, compared the matter to the beatific bliss of a dance (Ta'anit 31a), where each dancer points to Him, may He be blessed, [as] with a finger, saying, "Behold, this is our Lord, [whom] we hoped for, we will rejoice and exult in His deliverance!"[230] for He has given us such a clear glimpse, and through this we will be delivered from embarking on a wayward path, and we will apprehend more easily our true eternal bliss.

This is what the composer of the Kaddish wished to inform us [when he wrote]: "May His great Name be magnified and sanctified." In my humble opinion, this does not seem to be a prayer, but rather a consoling pronouncement to those who are mournful in spirit and broken in heart. He calls aloud: "My brothers, do not grieve that we have buried these holy limbs for storage in the hidden places of the earth, for now He will tell Jacob[231] that the one now buried will again rise and live in great ease when the time that His blessed Name will be magnified and sanctified arrives, and all will apprehend Him eye to eye. When will this be?

"In the world which is destined to be renewed,"[232] which will be renewed as an eagle its youth,[233] "and to resurrect its dead in it,"[234] viz., in that new world, the dead will rise and live, and the new creation of creatures will be "in order to raise them to eternal life,"[235] viz., that through their rising and resurrection to the redeemed world, these [renewed] creatures will find it easier to raise themselves still further and to approach in the end to the First Cause, may He be blessed, Who is [the Source] of Eternal Life.

All this too is declared in the simple Kaddish [recited] at the end of each prayer, but in a different style: "May His great Name be magnified and sanctified in the world which He created according to His will," viz., May it be His will that the intensity of His holiness and providence be soon proclaimed in this current corrupted world as well, which He created according to His will (as a woman recites the blessing "Who created me in accordance with His will," viz., even though according to human conceptions it would have been possible for her to have been created in a superior (*yoter nivhar*] form, but this is how it was accomplished, according to His will, may He be blessed, which is exalted beyond human comprehension). This will come to pass "in your lives and in your days and in the lives of the entire House of Israel, rapidly and in the near future," etc.[236]

The Purpose of the Resurrection of the Dead

Thus, all the problems we raised at the start of our discussion of this matter have been resolved. As to the question of the purpose of the resurrection of the dead, we may answer that this is in order to perfect the soul in greater wise, a matter which is impossible in the current world, since creation is not yet sufficiently matured, as we have explained. For in every cycle the world is perfected in greater measure than before, in [both] its material and spiritual aspects, [aspects] which are closely and inextricably intertwined, aside from the Fall in both, which Adam caused by his eating of the Tree of Knowledge. It is also impossible that this should come to pass in the spiritual world after death, for that is not a world of "doing" where a person may by his deeds perfect himself to shine with the light of life; but in the new world to come [both] the body and the soul will be purified, and will be more pure and holy than was Adam before he sinned.

The Life of the Soul After Resurrection

And in regard to the question we raised [above], as to whether the [dead] will live again on the earth in order to once again suffer the agony of death, our sages, may their memory be blessed, already solved this for us in the statement with which we began our discussion, but with their sharp eyes they saw further,[237] viz., from the fourth resurrection of the dead to the fifth, saying:

"The righteous which the Holy One, blessed be He, will in the future restore to life," viz., in the soon-to-come fourth resurrection, "will not return to their dust, as [Scripture] states, 'He will call him holy, all who are written for life in Jerusalem'[238]— just as the holy exist forever, so too they will exist forever. And if you ask, what will the righteous do"—at the time of the terrible destruction of the world, "during those years during which the Holy One, blessed be He, renews His world," viz., at the destruction of the fifth world, in order to renew His world as the sixth resurrection?

"The Holy One, blessed be He, produces eagles' wings for them"[239]—this symbolizes the painless separation of the soul from the body as that which occurred at the ascension of Elijah to heaven, when all the parts of his body and soul returned to the Original Foundation, may He be blessed. [This would have been the lot of man] had not Adam sinned, a death which our sages, may their memory be blessed, elsewhere termed "death with a kiss."[240] That is, because of the great desire and pleasure which the two, [God and man,] have at their "kiss," to draw near each other, the human partner will experience no pain at the separation [of the soul from the body].

This will be the common experience of humankind after the resurrection of the dead, when they will anticipate with joy and rejoicing the day of their separation [from material existence], to hover and flit with wings of flame without pain or suffering at all, as [Scripture] states, "Therefore we will not fear when the earth is changed, though mountains topple into the sea."[241]

This is the meaning of the end [of our sages' statement]: "And if you say that there will be pain in the separation of the body from the soul," as it is now, "the verse states, 'and those whose hope is in God,' viz., those who hope then to return in joy, will regain strength through this hope; [that is, to the strength] which they have in the fifth cycle will be added the greater strength which will come to them in the sixth cycle. In their knowledge of this, that their death, then, is [merely intended] to bring them to [eternal] life, they will lift wing like an eagle, and rise in joy and great rejoicing."

Even greater consolation for a person of the present cycle may be gained from the verses from the Prophets with which we introduced our discussion.

"Who are you that you are fearful?"[242] That is, [the verse states,] Who are you—[one] whom God has brought to being— that you should fear yourself,[243] when "you see that man must die,"[244] and when you see "mortals who fare like grass"[245] under clods of earth?

Can you not recognize yourself;[246] "do you forget God your Creator?"[247] Did He in His mercy and unending wisdom create you in order that you should die and cease to exist?

Moreover, "for I am God," Who is omnipotent, "Who stretched out the heavens and made firm the earth."[248] Is it then impossible for Me to create a new heaven and a new earth for you? Therefore, in order that you might forget all this, "you live in constant dread of the rage of the oppressor,"[249] viz., utter, eternal destruction—"but where is the rage of the oppressor?"[250] Is it not the case that wherever you see decay in the world you see that decay is the cause of renewed life?[251]

The thought of death can frighten you in two ways: (1) the pain of separation [of body and soul] at the moment of death, (2) if you are of the opinion that there is no life after death.

Regarding the first, [the prophet] declares: "quickly the crouching one is freed"[252]—the pain of death is not as great as one thinks; how could this be, inasmuch as death obliterates feeling, and it is only through the senses that we feel pain? But the Holy One, blessed be He, arranges matters so that one does not feel much pain at the time of separation [of body and soul], and that time does not long endure, but rather the ties that bind body and soul quickly open.

And regarding the second fear, I say to you, this too you must ignore, for "he will not die for the Pit,"[253] he will not cease to exist as a cloud [dissipates] with the wind, his soul will not lack sustenance after its separation [from the body], after which the soul will obtain its sustenance from the palace of the King, may He be blessed.

Or perhaps you are concerned that at the time of death, when terrible waves of thought storm through you tumultuously at the whirlwind of separation, or perhaps then, in that whirlwind, your soul will sink and drown, and your thoughts [disappear] into that sea of confusion.[254]

I come to you in the Name of God and say to you in His Name: "For I am God,"[255] Who calms and quiets the sea[256] and the stormy waves which storm as they will—I am God Who, with the strength of My arm, quiets them from [attacking] you.

So will it be at the time of your death, that you not sink in the tumult of those waves, and so too will it be at the death of the entire world and its destruction, which will occur before the resurrection of the dead by a fiery flood or a watery flood, terribly destructive, by which the world will receive a strong blow, and all will cease to exist in a moment in order to return to flower and bud again to new life, more beautiful than its present form.

God of Hosts is His Name, for He is Master of all Deeds, Lord of all Souls; blessed are You, Who returns souls to dead bodies, and therefore only the living, the holy congregation, can give thanks to You;[257] life and bliss will surround you in this [world] and the [world] to come, Amen!

ACKNOWLEDGEMENTS

I would like to acknowledge the courteous assistance of Dr. Diane R. Spielmann and the staff of the Leo Baeck Institute, the staff of YIVO Institute of Jewish Research, the Jewish Room of the New York Public Library, and the library of the Jewish Theological Seminary of America, and, as usual, the staff of the Mendel Gottesman Library of Yeshiva University, and especially, in this instance, Rabbi B. Mandelbaum and Mssrs. Zalman Alpert, Marie Center, David Crugnola, and Zvi Erenyi. My thanks also to Dr. Gene Gaffney of the American Museum of Natural History, and to Dr. Richard T. White.

NOTES

1. According to A. Berliner; see his "Die beiden Gedaljah in Obersitzko," *MG WJ* 50 (1906), pp. 215-219, see p. 216. The *Encyclopedia Judaica* article on R. Baruch Isaac, R. Israel's son, reports that he was born in 1812 while his father served in Wronki (vol. 11, cols. 290-291), but I have been unable to locate the source for this report, and the article on R. Israel himself merely places him in Wronki from 1821 (ibid., p. 293), apparently following A. Heppner and J. Herzberg, *Aus Vergangenheit und Gegenwart der Juden und der jüdischen Gemeinden in den Posener Landen,* Koschmin, 1909, p. 1016, n. 12.

2. See previous note.

3. Not to be confused with Colmar in Alsace, which also had a Jewish community.

4. According to Heppner and Herzberg, he served for six years in Chodziesen, around 1835, and Echt places him there from 1826 to 1837. The *Encyclopedia Judaica* article on his son Baruch Isaac has him elected to succeed

his father there in 1833, but prevented from doing so because of R. Akiva Eger's opposition to an unmarried youth of 21 doing so. Did R. Israel continue on for another four years because of this?

5. At present the main sources for his time in Danzig are Abraham Stein, *Die Geschichte der Juden zu Danzig*, Danzig, 1860, Max Aschkewitz, *Zur Geschichte der Juden in Westpreussen*, Wissenschaftliche Beiträge zur Geschichte und Landeskunde Ost-Mitteleuropas n. 81, Marburg, 1967, and Samuel Echt, *Die Geschichte der Juden in Danzig*, Leer, Ostfreisland, 1972. Unfortunately, the later accounts draw from Stein for estimates of R. Lipschitz's influence in Danzig, but he is not a reliable witness as far as R. Lipschitz is concerned; as a Reform rabbi who clearly wanted the post himself, and, indeed, served in Danzig for a few years after Lipschitz's death, he denigrates his successor as out of touch with the needs of the time and the community, and labels his commentary as unoriginal and of no scientific value. However, despite this, Echt writes of his "grossen Wissen, philanthropisches Tun and asketischen Lebenswandel" (p. 251, n. 42). I hope to take up this issue at another time.

6. Echt, *Geschichte*, p. 46.

7. See Serayah Dablitski, "Ba'al Tif'eret Yisrael ve-Tzava'ato," *Hama'ayan* 11 (5731), 28-44.

8. According to his son, Baruch Isaac, in his eulogy on his father, printed in *HaMagid* 4 (1860), pp. 170-171, subsequently incorporated into his introduction to his father's *Tif'eret Yisrael*.

9. Rabbi Lipschitz is not the first one to have done so; this suggestion was made at the end of the eighteenth century in *Sefer ha-Berit*; see Ira Robinson, "Kabbala and Science in *Sefer ha-Berit*: A Modernization Strategy for Orthodox Jews," *Modern Judaism* 9 (1989): 275-288. After his time, the great *posek*, Rabbi Shalom Mordecai Schwadron of Berzhan (the MaHaRShaM) mentions this possibility in his *Tekhelet Mordechai*, Bereshit 2. Rabbi Kaplan merely continues in this tradition.

Rabbi Lipschitz's *derashah* has never been translated before, but an adaptation of the last section, that dealing with fossils, appeared in *Challenge: Torah Views on Science and Its Problems*, edited by Aryeh Carmell and Cyril Domb (New York: Association of Orthodox Jewish Scientists, 1976), pp. 132-135.

10. These passages are from his *Recherches sur les ossements fossiles*, and are taken from Herbert Wendt, *Before the Deluge*, translated from the German by Richard and Clara Winston, Garden City: Doubleday, 1968, pp. 97-98.

11. Translation follows Rabbi Lipschitz's interpretation in the last section below; see pP. 121-122, below.

12. Isaiah 4:3

13. Psalms 46:3.

14. Isaiah 40:31.

15. This passage is interpreted in the last section of the sermon.

16. Deuteronomy 30:19.

17. Ibid.

18. Avot 4:22.

19. Jonah 4:10.

20. Psalms 36:7.

21. Psalms 90:12.

22. Numbers 27:7.

23. Exodus 30.18. The stand, of course, supports the basin, and thus *kan-ken* can be interpreted as implying "firmness," which then leads to the meaning of "truth, veracity."

24. See Psalms 90:12.

25. As set forth in Leviticus 23:15-16.

26. A conflation of Isaiah 66:23 and Exodus 34:23.

27. Isaiah 45:23.

28. Deuteronomy 16:9.

29. Leviticus 25:10.

30. An allusion to Ecclesiastes 9:5.

31. I Kings 8:12 = II Chronicles 6:1.

32. Psalms 16:11.

33. Psalms 36:10.

34. Isaiah 53.7.

35. Ecclesiastes 7:15.

36. From the Yigdal hymn.

37. Psalms 91:16, recited during the Sabbath morning prayers.

38. An allusion to Psalms 126:2.

39. Psalms 118:17.

40. Ibid.

41. Ibid.

42. Psalms 118:18.

43. Ibid.

44. Psalms 118:19.

45. Ibid.

46. See *Genesis Rabbah* 9:5; R. Meir apparently interpreted *me'od*, "very," as *mavet*, "death."

47. Psalms 126:6.

48. Psalms 118.20.

49. This theme appears already in the Zohar, see Elliot Wolfson, "Left Contained in the Right: A Study in Zoharic Hermeneutics," *AJS Review* 11 (1980), pp. 27-52, and idem., "Light Through Darkness: The Ideal of Human Perfection in the Zohar," *HTR* 81 (1988), pp. 73-95.

50. Psalms 102:27.

51. Or: "transmigrations." This may prefigure his "argument from paleontology" below.

52. An allusion to Genesis 3:6.

53. Psalms 104:29.

54. Ibid.

55. All these citations are from Psalms 104:29–30.

56. Psalms 104:31.

57. Ibid.

58. Psalms 104:32.

59. Ibid.

60. Psalms 104:33.

61. Ibid.

62. A concise statement of the first law of thermodynamics!

63. Ecclesiastes 3:14.

64. Or: "in nature," i.e., that anything in nature will not be annihilated.

65. Ecclesiastes 3:14.

66. A poetic statement of Cuvier's position!

67. Ibid.

68. Ibid.

69. An allusion to Avot 4:22.

70. Using the German word.

71. Genesis 2:6.

72. II Samuel 14:14.

73. Ibid. Translation follows the sense of the author's use of the passage.

74. Ezekiel 37:12.

75. All from Job 8:18–19.

76. Psalms 92:14.

77. Ibid.

78. Ibid.

79. Lamentations 3:23.

80. Ibid.

81. An allusion to Deuteronomy 20:19.

82. An allusion to Psalms 36:10.

83. An allusion to Deuteronomy 6:7.

84. Psalms 23:1.

85. Psalms 23:2.

86. Ibid.

87. An allusion to Deuteronomy 8:17.

88. A reinterpretation of Psalms 23:3, usually rendered "He restores my soul." Rabbi Lipschitz relates *yeshovav* (*pollel* of *shuv*), "to bring back," to *shovav,* "to go astray."

89. Psalms 23:3.

90. Ibid.

91. Psalms 23:4.
92. Ibid.
93. Ibid.
94. Printed editions have "37."
95. Psalms 22:30.
96. Proverbs 16:15.
97. Psalms 23:5.
98. Ibid.
99. Ibid.
100. An allusion to Psalms 139:21.
101. Psalms 23:5.
102. Ibid.
103. An allusion to Psalms 116:13.
104. Psalms 23:6.
105. Ibid., taking *ve-shavti* literally; it is often rendered as though it were *ve-yashavti*, "and I will dwell," see Targum and NJPS.
106. Ibid.
107. An allusion to Psalms 84:8.
108. An allusion to Exodus 28:11.
109. An allusion to Exodus 28:36.
110. An allusion to Canticles 8:10.
111. Taken from Exodus 3:8, 17, etc.
112. Genesis 4:10.
113. Genesis 9:6.
114. Genesis 9:5.
115. Genesis 17:14.
116. Ecclesiastes 12:7.
117. Psalms 31:20.
118. Psalms 17:14-15.
119. Psalms 16:10-11.
120. Leviticus 20:20.
121. Numbers 15:31.
122. Non-Jewish descendants of Noah.
123. See Kiddushin 32b for the phrase.
124. Isaiah 60:21.
125. Sanhedrin 10:11.
126. Sanhedrin 44a.
127. Psalms 18:29.
128. Proverbs 20:27.
129. Job 31:2.
130. Ecclesiastes 12:7.
131. Reading with ed. princ. השכל נותן; current editions lack the *nun*.

132 . Following ed. princ.; current eds. read שכיתפרדז, a misprint for שכשיתפרדו.

133 . Referring to the phrase used in the two versions of the Ten Commandments on Sabbath in Exodus 20:8 and Deuteronomy 5:12.

134 . Psalms 18:29.

135 . Psalms 34:21.

136 . Exodus 24:10.

137 . The first three are categories of soul, according to the Zohar; see Zohar 1:206a, 2:141b; also R. Isaiah Hurwitz, *Shenei Luhot ha-Berit* 1:9b. The latter two are Lurianic.

138 . Referring to the bone which remains as the seed for the resurrection of the body in Messianic times; see *Leviticus Rabbah* 18, ed. Margulies, pp. 394 f., *Genesis Rabbah* 28:3, ed. Theodor-Albeck, p. 261, and Tosafot, Bekhorot 8a, s.v. *tarnegolet.* For other references, see Zohar, ed. Margoliot, 1:137a, nn. 9-10. Kaplan himself discusses the function of this bone; see p. 36.

139 . Literally, "bones."

140 . Literally, "the time of joining," i.e., when the constituent elements are joined, either in one's earthly existence or at the time of the resurrection of the dead.

141 . Reading, with ed. princ., ידועים; current eds. have יודעים.

142 . Literally, "have been between our fingers."

143 . Gittin 56b.

144 . *Ecclesiastes Rabbah* 1:34.

145 . The seven-day period of mourning after the death of a member of one's immediate family.

146 . Ecclesiastes 7:20.

147 . Numbers 15:31.

148 . Ibid.

149 . An allusion to Leviticus 12:3 f.

150 . The quotation is not exact; the Talmudic passage refers to "those who sin with their bodies," which is explained later in various ways. One explanation, that of Rav, is that this phrase refers to sexual sin. From this Rabbi Lipschitz apparently infers that all those liable to *karet* fall into this category.

151 . Quoting II Samuel 14:14.

152 . As a dybbuk.

153 . See Gittin 57b. I cannot locate the exact reference in the *Shelah.*

154 . This apparently refers to the first edition, entitled *Hosen Rav,* published in Danzig in 1843, two years before this sermon was delivered. Curr. eds. 180a is a misprint; the reference is to his notes on Mishna Qiddushin. 4:14, in his excursus on miracles.

155 . An allusion to Isaiah 44:5.

156 . Citing Psalms 37:20.

157. Isaiah 43:7.

158. Isaiah 57:16.

159. Jeremiah 32:27.

160. Numbers 11:23.

161. Sanhedrin 91a.

162. This refers to a Talmudic statement in Pesahim 5a, where the rabbinic deduction from one letter of a Biblical text is taken to cancel the deduction from another; the Talmud suggests that it would have been better for the Torah not to have used either letter, and saved itself the trouble of canceling what it had proposed. The sentence entered Yiddish as an expression for unnecessary duplication.

163. An allusion to Avot 4:17.

164. Christoph Wilhelm Hufeland (1762-1836) published a number of editions of his *Makrobiotik*, starting from 1797 and again in 1805 and 1823; another was published in 1842 in Berlin after his death. Other editions were published after 1845. Few copies of this volume remain in libraries; all that I could determine is that Rabbi Lipschitz did not use the 1823 edition.

165. Mishnah Sanhedrin, chap. 10.

166. A hint rather than a full Rabbinic *midrash.*

167. Deuteronomy 32:39.

168. Ibid.

169. Isaiah 26:19.

170. Daniel 12:2.

171. Daniel 12:13.

172. Was this addressed to some important personage who attended Rabbi Lipschitz's sermon? Elsewhere he addresses his audience as "brothers."

173. Job 37:18.

174. Psalms 119:34.

175. An allusion to Isaiah 21:10.

176. An allusion to the windows of Solomon's Temple as described in I Kings 6:4.

177. Note that from here on Rabbi Lipschitz's talmudic citations become less exact. Was he writing under time pressure? Note that this sermon was published in 1845, the same year as the sermon was delivered.

178. The passage is actually attributed to R. Qetina.

179. An allusion to Sotah 40a.

180. 3:8-9.

181. Genesis 1:5.

182. Literally, "in the round."

183. *Leviticus Rabbah* 25:4.

184. Genesis 2:3.

185. Genesis 8:22.

186. Psalms 25:14.
187. Isaiah 24:19.
188. Isaiah 24:23.
189. Isaiah 34:4.
190. Isaiah 51:6.
191. Isaiah 65:17.
192. Ecclesiastes 1:4.
193. Psalms 148:6.
194. Exodus 21:6.
195. Leviticus 25:46.
196. So ed. princ; curr. eds. give the date in Hebrew letters אלף ותת״יז.
197. Clearly, Rabbi Lipschitz refers here to Georges Léopold Cuvier (1769-1832) and not his younger, less famous brother Frédéric (1773-1838). Cuvier, a French-German paleontologist, championed the catastrophic theory of "periodic extinctions." Most of his books and articles were written in French. According to a recent estimate, "there is no complete bibliography of Cuvier's works; one that included all the reprints and translations would probably run to 300 titles" (*Dictionary of Scientific Biography*, ed. by Charles Coulson Gillispie, New York, Scribners, vol. III, p. 527). It is probably impossible at this point to determine from which book or article Rabbi Lipschitz drew his information. It is clear, however, that his source was German and not French because he transliterates the *v* in Cuvier with a Hebrew *fé*.
198. My thanks to Dr. Gene Gaffney of the American Museum of Natural History in New York for help in identifying this creature.
199. An allusion to Genesis 3:20.
200. Hagigah 12a.
201. Genesis 1:2.
202. Literally, "a handsbreadth," referring to the expression that one "reveals a handsbreadth and conceals two" in regard to mystical matters.
203. Psalms 148:8.
204. Ezekiel 37:9. This chapter contains the prophecy of the dry bones.
205. Genesis 8:1.
206. Genesis 2:7.
207. The "crowns" which appear on certain letters of the Hebrew Bible from which halakhic and kabbalistic secrets may be derived; see Menahot 29b.
208. Psalms 105:8.
209. See pp. 78-79 above.
210. Psalms 90:2. The conventional translation is "Forever and ever You are God." Rabbi Lipschitz takes the idiom *me-'olam 'ad 'olam*, "forever and ever," literally "from world to world."
211. I Chronicles 29:10; Rabbi Lipschitz again interprets the idiom literally.

212. An allusion to Psalms 23:3.

213. Psalms 48:15, and interpreting "evermore" as "on worlds."

214. Psalms 72:16.

215. Proverbs 4:18.

216. Ibid., more usually translated "ever brightening until noon" (NJPS), but taken more literally here.

217. Malachi 3:23.

218. Presumably his obligations under natural law. Rabbi Lipschitz was writing during the heyday of Western European liberalism.

219. An allusion to Genesis 1:16.

220. Psalms 138:6.

221. Exodus 33:20.

222. Berakhot 33b = Megillot 25a = Niddah 16b.

223. Citing Deuteronomy 8:17.

224. An allusion to Isaiah 6:3.

225. From the Kedushah.

226. Isaiah 6:3.

227. Canticles 2:9, which is referred to repeatedly in the next lines.

228. Ibid.

229. An allusion to Isaiah 52:8.

230. Isaiah 25:9.

231. An allusion to Numbers 23:24.

232. Another quotation from the Mourner's Kaddish recited at the burial.

233. An allusion to Psalms 103:5.

234. Another citation from the Kaddish.

235. Further on in the special Mourner's Kaddish.

236. From the Kaddish.

237. Rabbi Lipschitz cites again the passage from Sanhedrin 92a with which he began, now interspersing his own interpretations.

238. Isaiah 4:3.

239. Ibid.

240. Moed Katan 28a = Bava Batra 17a.

241. Psalms 46:3. The word *hamir*, which NJPS renders "reels," has been translated in accordance with Rabbi Lipschitz's general use of the passage.

242. Isaiah 51:12; NJPS translates: "What ails you that you fear?"

243. Or: "your essence," i.e., your essential nature, mortality.

244. Isaiah 51:12.

245. Ibid.

246. Reading עֵת as אַתְּ, with ed. princ.

247. Isaiah 51:13.

248. Ibid.

249. Ibid.

250. Ibid.

251. See above, pp. 84-85.
252. Isaiah 51:14.
253. Ibid.
254. An allusion to Isaiah 51:15.
255. Isaiah 51:15.
256. An allusion to Isaiah 51:15.
257. An allusion to Isaiah 38:19.

The following is a reproduction of the first printing of the *Derush Or ha-Hayyim*, which appeared at the end of the *Nezikin* volume of Rabbi Lipschitz's commentary on the Mishnah, published in Danzig in 1845.

רסו

אור החיים

ואנחנו נשא ה' אלהינו כביד , ובעורתו ית' נפתח שפתי משרים .

אנוכי אנוכי הוא מנחמכם . מי את ותיראי
מאנוש ימות ומבן אדם חציר ינתן ; ותשכח ה'
עושיך נוטה שמים ויוסד הארץ ; ותפחד כל היום
תמיד מחמת המציק כאשר. בונן להשתית - ואיה
חמת המציק ? מיהר צועה להפתח ·ולא ימות לשחת
ולא יחסר לחמו - ; ואנוכי ה' אלהיך רוגעסים , ויהמו
גליו - ה' צבאות שמו (ישעי'נ"א פי"ב) .
תנא דבי אליהו , צדיקים שעתיד הקב"ה להחיותן, אינן
חוזרין לעפרן ; שנאמר קדוש יאמר לו כל הכתוב לחיים
בירושלים , מה קדוש לעולם קיים , אף הן לעולם
קיימין . ח"ת אותן שמים שעתיד הקב"ה לחדש בהן
עולמו , צדיקים מה הן עושין ? הקב"ה עושה להס
כנפים כנשרים ושטין על פני המים ; שנאמ' ע"כ
לא נירא בהמיר ארץ , במוט הריס בלב ימים .
שמא תאמר יש להם צער ? ת"ל וקווי ה' יחליפו
כח , יעלו אבר כנשרים , ירוצו ולא ייגעו , ילכו
ולא יעפו - . (סנהדרין דצב"ח) .

23*

דרוש אור החיים

האדם שהוא נראה תמיד אשר תמיד בין מות לקיים תעוף —
מקוייב תמיד להעמיד דבר זה מנ׳עיניו, אם רוצה להבליג א״ע
בטמים ובארץ . ואעפ״כ צריך שישגיח ביותר על קיון ; דהיינו
לבלי להעביר אפי׳ רגע אחד מלפני עיניו קיומו הכלקי ; ותמיד ישאב
א״ע כדבר קי וקים, שלא ימח לעולם . יוזהו שאמר הכתוב הקיים
והסות כתתי לפניך , ר״ל סותך וחייך העקדתי בקרוב סוד
להמגיחך ; אבל , ובקרת בקיים, בקר לך קיך התמידי
לשום עיניך עליו בטרטות פוד . דראו אקי ! אנכי כלטווינו
סתה״ק וסקד״ל להביט תמיד בלצ שוקט לתחת עיני השוגא היותר
גדול של קייבו . — פעמיס רבות או כל רגע
כעמיד לסכיכו מעמדיכו בטעה האקרונה , אשר נה בכך כתהתק
סהארץ , כמ״ש על כרקך אתה מת . יוזהו שאקז״ל
[שבת קנג״א] שוב יום אקד לפכי מיתתך ; ושאלו וכי אדם
יודע באיזה יום ימות ? והשיבו ישוב היום פן ימות למחר .
ע״כ לשון הגמ׳ . אולם ק׳ למה אז״ל למחר ,וכי היום אכו בטוקי׳
אבל מב׳ טעמים אמרו לשון זה . (1) דמפכי שהתשונה שהאדם יעשה
ביום אקרון שלו,אינו יכול לעשות רק במהומה ובהבך ; וא״כ איזה כח ?
יפול להיות לתשונה שיעשה אותה בטעה שהוא בעלמו בקמעו
אינכ אבל עלמו ; (2) ומפכי שהאדם הקל בדעת , יקשב , הכי
אפשר שהיום כבר אמות ? הלא לא ארגיש עדיין בתוך גופי אפי׳
רגוס מעט מהמיתה ? לכן אמרו לכו מאהביבו האמיתיים בישוב
הדעת , לו יהא כדבריך , עכ״פ ישוב היום פן ימות למחר,
ומה הכל יכול להתהוות בין ה׳יום למחר , והלא בתיב בין לילה
הי׳ ובין לילה אבד . אולם אות מקשבת המיתה , אם תעוף
תמיד לעיכי האדם , הוא תועלת גדול לגוף.ולנפש . לגוף,
שעי״ז ימעט כאב הרגשתו לתקסורי׳ ולהשפלת הכבוד כשיקלרו לו
בעולמו ; באמרו לכפשי,למה אכי חעגה ותבער כפשי כל כך על דברים של
עולם קלוס,אשר ע״כ בסוף . אעזבכו , ואלה הדברים לא יועילו לאמכוע
פרידתי מטכו . ועוד תועלת שני יש׳ג בגוף שעי״ז , הוא כוטע
יותר בטוח מהקב״ה ,כמ״ש קז״ל[חולין דה״כ] אדם ובהמה תושיע ה׳,
אין הקב״ה מושיע אלא לאדם שמשים א״ע כבהמ׳, שאיכה מרגשת .
ועוד תועלת שליטי לגוף , שע״י שיעמיד תמיד לפכי עיכיו מעמדו בשעה
אקרונה, תתקרר האימה מלפכיו בעת בואו , ולא יתבהל ולא יקרה
כשיבוא לבסוף , ובמפוקת כפס יכין א״ע עליו כל רגע .
אבל תועלת הכפש שירוויק האדם עי״ז , גדול ורס מאד;
שע״י שיוכור תמיד שהמיתה , יכהה וישקע להב הילר בקרכו;
וגם כל רוק גאה וגאון שעל ידיהן יקטא האדם , גם הם יכנשו

בלבנו ; וי חמר גי"כ מלאחו בקדשי קדשים של צרהק, הם הסוקים שהם
ממטל לשכל אנושי ; דתמ"ד חבור ההפסד הגדול שאפשר שיתהוה
לו שם בטולם הכלקי , אם לא ישמור מצות הי' אלהיו .

ולכן התחכן המטורר *לסגות ימיכו כן הודע ; אלת כן *
כ"ל שהוא מלשון כן נכות כלספיד דוברות , שהוא מלשון קוזק , כמו הכיוד
וכמו ; ר"ל הכל יודעים שימותו , ואותרים נפשהם שימותו , ור'עמ"כ
בארתה שעה עלמה קוטאי . — אבל הודיענו שכספור בתוזק הכוונה
את כל יום ויום שיזקל מלבכ נו מימיו ולא נרגים , שעל כנפיהם
ישאונו ימיכו לאט לאט לשתים לעולם אחר ; ואם כן אקמוב בטמעכה
פניתית בטומק הלב , אז ידעתי כי ביום הראותי פני אלהים קיים
נסוף , אביא אליך ה' לנב הכמים .—

*וונה *מקד מהטטמים שלוותכו תה"ק לספוד ספירת העומר , *
דהיינו לכתו שהלאום הקדוש סוסרת מעת לדתה , דהיינו קיום
לאתם מקלרים ז' שבועות ; כן גם אתה אדם תספור קלקי קיך
קיום שכולדת ז' שביעיית ; וכמ"ש מהקל קרקם בקקה , ר"ל
קיום שקרקם היל"הר התקיל לכקוף בכשמתך שהיא קקה וגם כלבנה ,
דהיינו מזמן לידתך , מאז תקל לספוד ז' שבועות , דהיינו ז' פעם ז' שכים .
וונה משום זה הטעם , משום דנבכל שנב' שכים , קיי האדם
משתכים , וקיוביו יתבשאו ויתרבו יותר שמה שהיו מקורם : א) נסוף
ז' שכים ראשונים כבר כגמל האדם מימי הילדות הראשונים ,ובתק"יב
כבר בקיכוך ; והאנות מקויבים מאז מעט מעט יותר להדריך בניהם
לעבודת ה' . (ב) בתקלת שנת י"ד , כבר כעשיכו בר מלוה
וכתקייבנו כבר בכל מלות התורה הלמ"מס [כמ"ו הרא"ש בכל ט"ו] .

(ג) בתקלת שנת כ"א כבר כתקייבנו בעונש ב"ד של מעלה [וכה פרשת
קולת] ; ולאשר כבר כתבנל שבליבו או היטב , לכן יקצלו עקב נו
בשמים יותר בקשבון מדוקדק .

(ד) בסוף ז' שכים הרביעיים , גופינו כבר כתבנל בתוזק כראוי , וקרבנו
למטקוי בן ל' לכח ; אז לכן כבר יותר כבוא לתוך המון האנשים
ונעסקי העולם , ונתנסה יותר בנסיונות , ויתרבו לכן קיובינו
לשאת ביותר עול העולם בלדק וביושר . — (ה) בסוף ז' שכים
הקמישיים , כבר קלי קיי המורגל של ע' שכים מוכק לקורינו
(ו) בסוף ז' שכים הששיים , כבר מוכק לקורינו קלי קלק הקיים ,
אם גם כקי בגבורות פ' שכים . (ז) בסוף בשכת הכ' הוא יובל ,
כבר השגת הראת העליין מפסגנת הקיים — ; הגוף מתקיל שאו
להתמוטט — וכבר תעמוד בפרשת הדרכים — ; שם תצעמוד
אקך הטובה , היא תה"ק , ותקרא לך וספרת לך , וספרתם
לכם , לטונתך ולטיבתכם תתקילו ימי הקיים ; אדם ! הכי עליין אתה
משוקע בטכרוגך מלרבי עולם עונר ? עורה ! עורה ! דטך
כבר כתקרר , שבלך כבר כתבל , ילרך כבר ירד מטה מטה

דרוש אור החיים

בעומק תרחב נפילת חייך : — כבר הוכל לחשוב בעלמך שא"א עוד לך
להתקיים זמן מרובה ; ולבן וקדשתם פ"ח , שבתו, הם אנשים
שכה ; לכל הספקות פתח תחתיל לדאות בעד שכובסת משמחך
בשולם האחר הבא לקראתך , כנר קרב העת שאד, ;
ובשנרגיל את עלמינו לחשוב כך תמיד שאו בלומן זה מהמציאן הקשר של
תמי יתה , ומהזכרון שקמו , כשאב אור וחיים .. אבל אעפ"כ בלבטוחסר
ביותר להשגית בעין שקוד על קייכו , דהיינן חין בלקיית שלמו ; זה יבשח
הרגשותיכו , ורודיעיכו היקר האמיתי של אדם ; דמה קשיבת יש בתיים ;
ואיזה , שפל ויקר יהיה לו אם לא , יתקיים לנצח ? הכי לא יהיה
קיים פה יותר גרוע מהמות דהסקיים יודעי' שיטותו ; והמתים אינם
יודעי' מאום ? — אולם החהלה לאלי' שמתוך
העכן האחוך של המות , הביח לנו הקרין נכולי האור הנסתר
תחתיו ; ה' אמר לשכון בערפל ; הקנ"ה רלה כך להמתיר
האור היקר של קיי הנלקית , ולקתלו בערפל , שלא יסיג האדם
באר היטב אופני החיות שם , כדי שלא תתבטל הבקירה בזיה ;
הרי זה כל מטקוי בריאת האדם לעולמו, שע"י בקירתו הקפשית, יהיה
הוא התוכליף פ"ע — .

עמום הוא המעמד ההוא — ואעפ"כ יאיר לעיניכו התכלות
מעט מאור ההוא ; שעם כל המסתר הגדול שמעמדיכו שם ,
אעפ"כ בוכל לבבר ת"ל שאבחכו שם קיים קיימים וכאמכים .
ממך אבינו שבשמים השגנו בל אלה ! כמ"ש, תודיעכו ארוק קיים
שובע שפקות את סכיך , כעימות בימיכך כלק ← שכחיה
שם עמך ; כי עמך מקור קיים באורך כראה שם אזר אמיתי.
וגם בחמונת הקעיקר הזה יש תועלת גדול לגוף , ולכפש ;
לגוף דאיך יערב לגוף אבול ושמות ושאר עגוני הכפש , אם ידע
בכפשו כי הוא כשה לטבק יובל , וסוף כל סוף כעשן תתום כפשו ;
אולם גם לכ פש אין לך תועלת גדול סחכו , כי בקיות הזמכיי, כראה
הרנה פעמים לצדיק אוכד בלדקו , ורשע ברשעו ילביק , ועי"ז
כמו ידי אדם החלט לילך בדרך התורה במקום שיפסד עי"ו פובנ
הגוף , או חרווחת ממון או , הכבוד ; אולם האמונה בהשארת הכפש
תהיה לו לאור בדרכו בעלמו , בידעו כי שם הוא מקום הגמול
והגוכע , וכי בעו'הז אי אפשר שיתחלמו הרשע או הלדיק כדי
שלא תתבשל הבקירה — ; וכמה לא ירווית גם בשצתו האקרונה
ע"י אקפתו בעיקרוה , שיתמתק לו עי"ו קרירות יסורי המות .
אולם אם גם הקיקר הזה עוד כל כך מושרש בלב שומעי
האהובים , אעפ"כ אקשוב כי יסמק כל לב ישראלי אם יביאו לו
רחיות קזקות כראי' מוקק על עיקר הזה אשר בלעדו אין לקשוב
בשום אופן בשום הצלחה שבעולם .

דרוש אור החיים   רס"ח

וְהֲרֵי גַם יְהוֹשֻׁעַ שֶׁלֹּא בַּ' מְרַגְּלִים לְהָאָרֶץ הַמְשׁוּבַּחַת לְרַגֵּל אוֹתָהּ ,
אַף אֲבָנֶךָ בָּבְטִיחַ הַקָּבַּ"אָ שֶׁהִיא אֶרֶץ זָבַת חָלָב וּדְבַשׁ,וּשֶׁיְּכַבְּשׁוּ אוֹ־ ; ־ן וְתֵ־ןָ
לֹא כַּשֶּׁלַח גַם אָנַחְנוּ בַּ' מְרַגְּלִים שֶׁלָּנוּ דְּהַיְינוּ קוּשְׁיְכוּ וּבַבְלִי,כֵּן
לְהָאָרֶץ הַחַיִּים הַיּוֹתֵר עֲשׁוּנָק הַהִיא , כְּדֵי לְחַזֵּק וּלְאַמֵּץ לְבֵינוֹ
בְּהֲאֲמוּנָה הַיְּקָרָה הַזֹּאת .

אֲבָל אַחֵי הָאֲהוּבִים , זֹאת הָעִיקָר שֶׁל הָאֲמוּנָה יֵשׁ בָּהּ חֲלָקִים :
(י) כָּל יִשְׂרָאֵל מְחוּיָּב לְהַאֲמִין שֶׁנַּפְשׁוֹ לֹא תִּתְחַפֵּשׂ אַחַר מוֹתוֹ :
(ב)סַקוּיָּיב כָּל אֶחָד גַ"כ לְהַאֲמִין שֶׁיֵּשׁ תְּחִיַּית הַמֵּתִים לְהַגּוּף הַמְכוּנָה
בְּשֵׁם [חוּיפסֶערְּסֶטעֶהוּנָג] בַּלַ"אָ .

וְעַל בַּ' מִינֵי הַתְחִי' יְרָמְזוּ כְּמִילוֹת הַפְּסוּקִים בְּתְפִלּוֹתֵינוּ מְחִיּ"ם
יַּקִים אֵל בְּרוּב חַסְדּוֹ , עִתִּים יַקִים אֵל בְּרוֹב חֲסַדּוֹ ; דַּרַ"ל ה'
יָמִים לֶעָתִיד הַנְּשָׁמָה — וְשׁוּב יַקִים לְנַסּוֹף גַם הַגּוּף . וְכַ"כ
אוֹרֶךְ יָמִים אַשְׂבִּיעֵהוּ וְאַרְאֵהוּ בִּישׁוּעָתִי , אוֹרֶךְ יָמִים וְגוּ' ,
דְּהַיְינוּ אֲרִיכוּת יָמִים בְּעוֹלָם הַנְּשָׁמוֹת , וְאוֹרֶךְ יָמִים הַגּוּפְנִי . וְכַ"כ
כָּל הַנְּשָׁמָה תְּהַלֵּל יָהּ הַלְלוּיָהּ , כַּ' ה' תַּ' לַ' ה' ; בָּרוּחַ וּבַגּוּף .
בַּ' פְּעָמִים כְּכָפְלוּ לָנוּ הַדְּבָרִים בְּתְפִלָּתֵינוּ , כְּדֵי לְהַשְׁרִישׁ בְּלִבֵּינוּ
הָאֲמוּנָה הַזֹּאת הַיָּפָה וִיפָה , לְאֲשֶׁר בִּלְעָדָהּ אֵין שִׂמְחָה וְהַנְנַלְבֵּ' כְּמַלְאֲךָ' בָּעוֹלָם.
לָכֵן חַל חַל תַּחְרְדוּ אַחַי הַזְּקֵנִים, אִם תִּרְאוּ כֹּחֲכֶם הוֹלֵךְ וְכִיסּוּק,וְכִי
אַתֶּם הוֹלְכִים וּקְרֵבִים לְמַעְקוּי כָּל אָדָם ; דְּעוּ ! לְעוֹלָם לֹא יִתְחַפֵּס
קַיי הָאָדָם — נָקִיָּה וְלֹא נִפְסַק לְעוֹלָם מַלְכִיּוֹת . ה' יַאֲמֵץ הַיּוֹם
כּוֹתִּיהַצָּעִיר לְהָאַ"ר אֶתְכֶם,וְיַאֲמֵץ גַ"כ כְּחֲכֶם הַיּוֹם לִהְיוֹת מוּתָרִים —
שָׁמְעוּ וּתְחִי נַפְשְׁכֶם :

אוּלָם הַתְּכוּנָכַת הַזֶּה הַיּוֹמַיִי תִּסְתָּעֵף לַגַ' חֲלָקִים :
(א) נִרְאָה לַנֵּר , שֶׁנִּשְׁמָתֵינוּ , דְּהַיְינוּ שֶׁלְּשֶׁלֶת מַקְצְבוּתֵינוּ —
גַם אַחַר הַמֶּוֶת יִהְיֶה תָּמִיד מִשְׁתַּלְשֵׁל וְהוֹלֵךְ עַד אֵין קֵץ וְסוֹף — .
(ב) נִרְאָה גַם לַנֵּר , אֵיךְ יִהְיֶה מֵעְמָד הַנְּשָׁמָה לְאַחַר הַמֶּוֶת ;
וְאֵיזֶה דָבָר שָׁעֶּעָס"כ יוּכַל אוֹ לְהַפְסִיק בְּעַצְמוּתוֹ אֲבָל הַנְבַּלְתִּי לְדִיק .
(ג) לְנַסּוֹף כְּנֵּר גַ"כ , שֶׁגַם הַגּוּף פַּ"אָ שׁוּב יָשׁוּב וִיקוּס לְקִיּוֹת

(א)

זֶה הָעוֹלָם קַיי טַבְעִיי' .
בָּרוּר כַּשֶּׁמֶשׁ עוֹמֵד לְפָנֵימוֹ אֱמוּנַכַת הַשְׁאָרַת הַנֶּפֶשׁ אַחַר הַמֶּוֶת ; וְהוּא
עֵדִים לָנוּ עַל זֶה ה' רְאִיּוֹת חֲזָקוֹת וּפְשׁוּטוֹת . וְהֵם (יׁ) מֵחְכוּ בְּעַצְמֵנוּ .
(ב)מֵהָעוֹלָם בִּכְלָלוֹ . (ג)מֵהַנִּבְרָאִים בִּפְרָטִיּוּת . (ד)מֵהַקָבַּ"ה לְבַדּוֹ .
(ה)מִתַּהַ"ק שֶׁנִּתְחַתְּמָה הָאֲמוּנָה הַזֹּאת בְּגוּסְפַּנְקָא שֶׁלֹּה , וְקִיּוּתוּ שֶׁל
הַקָבַּ"ה אֱמֶת . וּמֵעַתָּה נְבָאֵר כָּל הָרְאִיּוֹת הַנַּ"ל אַחַת לְאַחַת .
(יׁ)מִמֶּנּוּ בְּעַצְמֵינוּ , דְּהַרֵי כָּל עֲצְיוּתֵינוּ וַעֲסְקֵינוּ , מַקְצְבוּתֵינוּ

דרוש אור החיים

ודימרינן הם כולם נאמן כאילו אכלנו בטומים שלעולם נמיה ; נדבר
במורגל למיתתו — ולא לנד שבאמתה שעה לביגו שזקט וכם ,
אלא הה' גם משתעשעי' ומעונני' חן , ויש נכלתינו נאמתו רנע
למלא שמיק מינו , כאילו נדבר שהתקלפת נגד , וטנכלבנ נגד אקר .
והכי זה לנדו אינכו כבר אות לאת כאמן על אמונה זו ! והרי זה וקריאא פכיטית
מהכשמה הדרה בתוכינו שאתליץ יותר למרחוק מעיני בשר , והיא תאמר בלאמ
אליכו , אל תירד אדם ! — לא תמות , ולעולם ולעד לא תגוע . —

*ובך אמר המשורר נרוח קדשו בהתעוטטו למעלה , לא אמות ;
ואם גם פ"א יפנשני זה אשר יקראוהו על אדניו מות , כי אחי' ,
ר"ל אז אתחיל לחיות באמת .

דאם רק אז הפרוכת העב הגופני יכפל ויתקפל לאחוריו ,
אז עם עינים פתוקות אספר מעשה יה — כי אז אשיג סודות
העולם — ומצוות חוקי התורה , אשר עתה בעולם הגופני לכל
בן מיתה לנכף ולעד ישארו סגורי' — ; אבל אז , העגן סר ואראה כל
סתורי אור — .

והמות בעצמו , אינכ מכנהו רק יסורי' מעט — ; ולכן יסד
יסרני יה אז בנעת המיתה , שיכאב לי קלת ; אבל לטות לא כתככי
הפקר , שיהיה ביכלתו לפנלסני ולאפסני — .

ולבן פתחו לי שערי לדיק , שאלך בדרך הלדק שבתחנה לפני
התח"ק ללכת בהם , וגם אבוא נם כאשר הורני ה' — אז אלדע
בנעתך , כי יבוא עת אשר אודה יה שבראת המות ; וכמ"ש בתורתו
של ר"מ על הפסוק וירא אלהים את כל עשה והנה טוב
מחד — והנה טוב מות — כי שם יאכל לדיק פרי מעשיו ,
ונח יבוא ברינה בושא אלומותיו — .

וגם המורא והפסד מהמות לא יקודני , כי זה השער לה' ,
לדיקים יבואו בו ; ר"ל אותו שיככו הנב"א מות , הוא השער אשר
על ידו ונו כיסע לפני ולפנים להיכל ה' , ולהשתעשע באור פני
אלהים חייט ; לדיקים יבואו בו , במנוקות הנפש ובלב אמיץ בלי
פקד ומורא , כי הוא הוא שער האור להדלקה נלקיית , לאור
בהור החיים — . זהו הרא" שלהבאהרת הנפש ממנו בעלמינו .

(2) אולם מלבד שמקמצנותיכו בעלמן נובל לבדד שלא נ כנוע וכהתאבם
לנכף , וכראמרן ; יש לנו ג"כ בירור על זה מהעולם בכללו — ;
דאם רק נתבונן על הטבע בכללה והתפעלותה , סונב סונב הולך
כחה — ; והן רחינו שכל הכדמה וכראה מגת , הוא עלמו יעמיד ויקומם חיים
קדשים — וכל נפילה בלד זה , הוא עלי" בלד אקר ; וכל הרקנה
והשקתה שישלט בנבראיה , יוליד בריאה קדשה לאור עולם .

הטבע תשאכה כל רגע , ותמראה בטלבום אקר ונתואר
אקר — ? כמ"ש, כולם כבגד יבלו , כלבוש תקליפס ויקלומו—

כל הטבע תתהפך , ותסתובב כגלגל , ותתראה שוב בתמונה אחרת
יותר עתיקא מ_תחלה , ולפעמים לריבה לזה כמה גלגולים — .

אמרו לי אחי האהובים , מי שלא ראה הזריעה מעולם , ויספרו
לו שנשמת האדם שאינה מתה , וגם יספרו לו שכשיקחו גרעון פרי
א' וניקולו תחת _ רגבי'. עד שירקב ויכלה , שאח"כ ילמח מהגרעון
הזה עץ כמה"ד למראה עם עלים הטובי' , ופרחים יפים , ופירות
מתוקי' , אשר נהם יהיו רננות גרעינים כדוגמת _את אשר הורקבה
תחת הרגבי' , מה יחשוב זה השומע ? ולא"ה מפני מיני החיית
הגבלה , של האדם , ושל העץ , הוא יאמין לכו ביותר ?

הלא יחשוב בעצמו שזה מעשה הזריעה שספרו לו הוא מעשה נדוי ·עלב
סכוייר ביופי אמרים ; ואעכ"פ יאמין יותר בהשארת הנפש ; דהכי אפשר
שאחר שנרקב וכתאחם הגרעון ישוב ·יעלה כיונק נרטיבות ילדות ,
ויתרבה עוד נרגבות מעתי' יותר משאר הי' בתחלה — ; ואעפ"כ כך הוא !

או כעתיד לפנינו אדם איטאלקי וסיצילען שלא ראה ולא שמע
מזורף ושלג וקרח מעולם ; אם זה יבוא למדיכתינו בחורף ויראה
אלפינו כל הבוראות ההם , והאילנות הינשות כעלמים , מה יחשוב
זה האדם ? הלא יאמר נלבו כאן מתה הטבע כמו אדם , ולא
תשוב עוד לאדן הקיים .

אבל הכי אין המות הכדמה הזה השולט בקורף נכל הטבע ,
רק סנת הקיים שלה ? ושינה שלה או בלישים כלון קיים בקורף , הכי
אינכו רק מכוקה, כדי לאסוף כחות קדשות לשוב באביב לימי כעיריה,
ולהתרחות בתפארת כפול מאשר עזנחה העולם ביתי הנליב ? כן גם
מיתתיכו אינכו רק כדי לשוב לקיים קדשים אחרים .

יוזהו שאמר הכתוב תסתיר פכיך מהתרן בקורף , יבהלון כל
הנרותים , ושכבו כולם כפגרים מתים — אבל אכי אומר תוסף
רוקם יגווען, שאפי' כשאירחה שיגווען, אלדע שעי"ז יתוסף רוקם;
ואפי' כשאירחס ואל עפרם ישובון , אלדע כי זה רק כדי שתשלף
שוב רוקך, רוח קייס, יגראון שוב , ותקדש פכי האדמה .

השגיחו ! מהרה יהי כבוד ה' לעולם באביב הנל , ויתראה
כנוד מלכותו , זהאילנות המתות האלו שוב יתקשטו ביזוק ילדות
רטוב , ויתהדרו עם פרקים יפים וסירות מהודרות שימילו ריק
עדנכ בעולם , אשר עי"ז הלפרים עפות אשר שקים בשינכם באויר
ירונו וישוררו על פאר העולם וכל אשר נו — עד כי ישמק ה' במעשיו.

לכן אם אראה נלד אקר, שיביט לארץ ותרעד, שיקרה לאדם
נרה או נס מיתה , שיגע בהרים של ההבלקה של אדם ויעשכו,
אעפ"כ לא אקרד , אבל אצירה לה' בחיי. ר"ל עבור הקייס אשר
נתן לי, שלא יקזור לטלו מסני, אזכרה לאלהי בעודי , כי עוד
אהיה כן לנכד ולא אתום . —

23**

דרוש אור החיים

(י)אבל גם בלי ראיה הזאת מכללות הטבע, שכל גוזיע' דמיוניית,
יוציא רק קיים קדמים ; יש לכו עוד ראיה ג' מכרואיות הפרטיים ,
שבכל יסוד ראשון חמוס נראיה לא יוכל להתאפס ולהסתקע לגמרי .
קח כא שום דבר שתרבה, כמאת אותו , ושסוק אותו , וצרוף אותו ,
ועשה עמו כל מה שתרבה , ולא יהי' ביכלתך לאפסו לגמרי . זא"כ,
איך יהי' היותר יקר והיותר אפרחי שבטבע ובככל הברואים דהיינו
נשמתו של אדם , גרוע מכולם , שיהי' אפשר שיתאפס לגמרי ?

*גם רחי' זו כתוב הדור הוא בכתבי קודם ; שהטע"ה אמר
ידעת' כי כל אשר עשה אלהים , הוא יהיה לעולם , ולא
יתאפס בטבע ; הן אמת צליו אין להוסיף שלא תוכל לעשות
לקי' בת ד' רגלים כנסים לעוף , או לעוף בת כנפים גם ד' רגלים ;
אבל גם שמבו אין לגרוע, כי בכל כחך לא תוכללגרוע מהעול' ולאפסו.
ולמה סידר הגזורא ית' כך עולמו ? ה"ט, זאלהים עשה שירא
מלפניו , לבלי לקטוח בגדו , שלא תקמוב שיהי' השאול בית מכוס
לך , ותחדמה שרק נע"הז יוכל הקב"ה לענטני , אבל כשאהי' בשאול
כתאפס ק"ו, ושם יהיה מקום מקלט שלי , שלא יסיגני יד ה'
לענטני שם ; לכן סדר לפניך כל הטבע באופן שלא תמס , למען
תדע כי מב"ש שהנכפם שהוא היותר קטוב שבעולם לא תתום נסוף. —
שמא תאמלי לאין הלך להב הנר שנכבנה ? זלאין עף הרטיבות
של הבגדים שנכבנסו וכתיינסו ? וח"כ על בריחך שים דבר בטבע
שיתום זיתאפס ?

על זה אשיב לך דע ! שהקב"ה נתן כח שואב באויר הרקיע
הנקרא אטמאספערא , שעל ידה שואב האויר כל הרטיבות והקמימות
או אד'ם הקיים אשר יתבאתו מהארץ לאפדים , עד שיגיעו למעלה
ויתארו שם את עלמן לענכים , ומשם יתרוקקו שוב להארץ בהמטר ,
וכמ"ש וד' יעלה מהארץ והשקה כל פני האדמה.

*וגם את הרחיה מלאכונה בהדברים הקיים וקיימים של תה"ק
בהתזכם' שאמר' האשה החכמ' להמע"ה על שלא רלה למחול
לאבשלום ; אמרה , כי מוד כמות , ר"ל מוך ק' שנה לא תאחר
פרסה שמכו כולנו סה זמכל קי זלמח שבעולם , שעתה קי
ומתעכניעע — הכל יהיה אז כאילו לא היה בעולם.

אבל הכי בי באמת כאנד הכל ? לא ! רק כמים הנגרים על
קרקע , אשר לא יאספו ולא בשאנו בידי אדם ; ואעפ"כ הנט
לאקר שעה על המקום שכזולו זהכה ינטה הארץ ! ולאין הלכו — ?
אבל רק בידי אדם לא נאספו , אבל עלו למרומים של הרקיע
זהרבה מהם שנטבנעו בארץ , גם מם יעלו ע"י אדים לרקיע , זמשם
יקוחו לרדת לארץ ע"י המטר ; אבל לא נאבדו .

וגמרה החכמה הכ"ל דבריה להמלך , ואמרה שכ"כ לא
יצא אלהי' כפא , לעקרו מצורת החיים ולאפסו ;
צבלתי ידק ממכו נדק , ר"ל אפי' אותו שבחקת רשע גמור
הוא , ולפי דעת הקלרה של אדם רחוי להדיקו מהוויתו , אפ"ה
הקב"ה ברוב רחמיו לא ידיקו ; ואפי' הכדמה מודק אינו נדק רק
לפני אדם , זלא לפניו ית' . ובזה יש חוכף גדולה לך המלך ,
שהדקת את אבנלום ולא חרלה להשיבו , ותעשה דבר שאינו דרך ה' זגם
לא דרך הטבע , שאין דבר שיתחאפס בה .

ואם אתה אחי החבוב תרלה לראות תחיית המתים עין בעין
התבונן התולעה הנקרא רויפע שתחיה איזה שבועות , הזל
ותתכוע ותאכל , עד שאח"כ תחקוזה הבצץ , ותארג סביב עלמה
בית לפר , ותתקשה בתוכו, ויהיה ביתה קנרה — וסם מונקת כמת ה'
או ו' שבועות — עד שאכי פתחיש בעלמי בית בילה כזאת תוך זמן
זה , וזמלאתי שם דבר אושקת דומה כמעופם ; אולם לאחר כלות
זמן התהווותו בתוך קליפתא , תנקר הבריאה הכ"ל הקליפה ויצא
לאור בריה קדשה עם כנפים מבריקים ויפים , וזשמעטטערליבג
קי שם ושמח יעוף למעלה הכה זהכה —

בך יהי' הסוף של קיי הרויבע שלך אדם בהקנר ; שם תתאר
עלמך לקיים אחרים — זמשם יגאלך ה' — כאשר אביך הרקמן
בעלמו אמר בי אכי ה' בפתקי את קברותיבם — ועם כנפי
להב תעוף או לשמים מחעל .

וזהו שאמר הכתיב באר היטב , אם יבלעכו ממקזמו ; ר"ל
להאדם , ובקם בו לא ראיתיך , שהכל יאחרו הרי הוא כאילו
לא רחיכוהו מעולם ; הן הוא משוש דרכו , ומעפר אחר
ילמקו ; בארץ השמיימי ישוב בעץ פורק לקיות ; וכמ"ש ג"כ
שתולים בבית ה' , בעה"ב , שם הוא שרש הקיים , וסם יעשו
פרי , אבל בקלרות אלהיכו דהיינו בעה"ז רק יפריחו , כפרק
שהוא עושה הככה לעשזת אק"כ פרי עץ הדר —

ולפע"ד זהו כמ"ש חז"ל בברבו' דמג"כ האי מאן דכפיק ביומי
ניסן וקזא אילני דמלבלבי , אומר בא"י אמ"ה שלא קיסר
בעולמו כלום , וברא בו בריות טובות ואילכות טובות
להתכאות בהן בנ"א . דתמוה דמה לכו להזכיר נהברכה
מבריות קיות שג"כ בבריב כרמין יפח,והרי עכ"פ הרי אינו מברך רק על
האלנות שרוחה אותן ? ותן ? ב', שם"יס להתכאות בהן בנ"א, איך ע"י קעטע
הירוק ירראה בחילנות יתנאו גם הבנ"א ?

אמנם העולם זבריותיה שעליה , תמיד עומדים יקד בקישור
אמין חדוד ; מקרה האחד הוא מקרה הב"ני ! בקורף , יהי' לא
לבד קירף בעולם , כ"א גם כל הבריות בו זהיו או רפוי

דרוש אור החיים

ידים ומושקעים בתרדמה ; וקפאון ונמיכות רוח ימשולו על הכל .
ואולם כאשר יגבע הקרן הראשון מהאביב על פני העולם , אז
שוב ישוב הכל להעלות כר החיים ; הכל נהטבע יקץ לקיי ילדות
חדשים ; כמ"ש קדשים לנקרים . ר"ל נכל נוקר יתרא' קיום חדש
בהטבע , ובכ קדם יתראה נו , רנה אמוכ תך ה' ; ואיך נאמן אתה
ה' ! שהלוויגו לטבע שלך בחורף כוחות העולם — , והנה תשלם
לנו באביב נפראלעבטע כפולים מה שהלווינו לה .
ולכן אחז"ל בפסחים [קינ"ב], כד קזיח שור שקור ביימי ניסן , ריש
תורא בדיקולא , סק לאגרי וסדי דרגא מתותך ; ר"ל לך
ונטה לך או מהלך ממול הנהמות , שעלולים להזיק או
ניהירות טבעם .

כל הנדוחים והנכ"א הם או כאתים לקיים יותר שלמות , –
לרפואה ולנריאות יותר שלמולשת ולקולשת , לשמחה ולעונג יותר
מלינן ולנכאות לב כפוף .

והישראלי שנכל השנויים שיקרו בטבע, תמיד ימלא נהן דנר אשר
יעוררו לנקש השלמת כפשו ; להכי כזקזי אילני דמלנלני , דהיינו
שיתהו על ענכי האילנות כמו לגנות קטנים רטונים — יזכר כי
גם האדם עץ השדה — גם זה האילן יבגד פ"א רטיבות שלו
נחורף שלו, דהיינו בזקנתו — ; אבל נסוף החורף ההוא יקץ לאביב
יותר יפה , וישוג לקיי כערות שוב ללנלב נקיים אקריים .

לבן אומר או , ברוך שלא קיסר בעולמו כלום , שלא
יניח נעולמו שום דנר להתאפם , ואותו הגזיעה והתרדמה שראינו
בהטבע בהקורף , הי' רק הכנה להשלמה שיבוח אקריו ; כי החסרון
הזה שראינו נהקורף בהטבע הוא אשר על ידו ברא הנריות טובות וקיות
הבם , שהם עתה יותר יפים ואמלי לב מאשר היו בשלהי הנליר ;
וגם האילנות הם עתה יותר טונות מאשר היו או , כי עתה שנו
לימי כעוריהן .

ומסיים בדבריו עיקר כוונתו בנרכתו , שבל זה כסדר כך מיוסד
נראשית ית' , כדי להתהנאות נהן בנ"א ; שעי"ז יקשוב האדם
ג"כ שהמיתה הנדמת שלו , ישאנו לקיים אקריים ; והעגן הרעם של
המות תשאכו כאליהו לשמים , לאור לפני ה' באור הקיים .

ובכן כנר יש לנו ג' רמיות קזקות על השארת כפשותנו ,
דהיינו , מושכ בעלמיכו ; ומהטבע בכלל ; ומהבנוּאים בפרטיות .
אבל למה לא נביא ראי' מהק'בה אביכו הטוב שנשמים , אחזן כל
הנשמות שקור כל הקי"ס ? כי עמך מקור קיים , באורך
נראה אור עלמיכו ג"כ .
הישך עאפין אקי שים בנמלא ה' אקד ? לכן ! אין שום בעל שכל

דרוש אור החיים   רע'א

בעולם שלא יאמין זאת , דהל"כ אי הוליא כל הטבע המסודרת
האת־לאור , כמו שנראה . א"כ אם תאמין כך , על כרחך לריך
אתה ג"כ להאמין שים השארה לנפש —

דאמור כ‎ה לי ידידי, הלא תענה,מהוא ה' פ — תשיבני , הוא עלם רם
ונישא , נשמת העולם וקיומתו, המקליא הכל,ומלא בכל מקום,והוא יוד ע
הכל , ולח כמתו אין סוף , ולטובו אין תכלית , ולגדרקתו אין
קן , ולכסו אין גבול ; ושכל המדות הללו ישנם בו ית' , מתברר לנו בכל
מפעלותיו ; ולכן לא יסתפק בזה שום אדם בעולם .

וערה אם נקשוב שהאדם כשיקות ח"ו תכלה נשמתו כעשן ,
א"כ השכל היקר שחנן ה' להאדם , יהי' רק להתליאו ולהשפילו
יותר מכל נהמת הארך ; דהנהם' כשמונקת תקת סכין של שקיע' ,
עדיין אינה יודעת שתוך רגע תתם וכלא הי' תהי' — ; והאדם
מתקלת העת שפתח עיניו , יודע היטב שא"א לו להנצל מהמות
שיפגשהו לבסוף ; וא"כ בקומו ובשכבו תענכו ותליקהו המקשנה
הזאת , שיהא אקריחו נוער לזה המעמד הנעלב :

והכי לוה הדליק לי הקב"ה להאדם אנוקת השכל , שיראה
בחורה רעתו ולראת הנורא' , שקיעתו , ותשכתו פ ואיה טוב'תו ,
ית' , ‏ קכמתו וידיעתו פ

שוב כראה בעולם במורגל,לא די שהלדיק אינו משתלם על לדקו,
כ"א גם הרבה פעמים יסבול לרות רבות ורעות ; והרשע כראה' במורגל לא
די שלא יענש , רק ילליק ברשעתו ויעריץ ; ואם נאמר , שמקרות
הלדיק אינו לכסיון , והלקת הרשע אינו הארכת אף , ושם נקיים
האחרים לא יותן שכר לוה ועונש לזה,א"כ איה היכולת ולדקות ה'
כמפורסם לכל פ

*ועל כל זה אמר המשורר הקדוש מזמור שלם . אמר , ה' רועי
לא אתסר ; ר"ל אני בהמה קטנה שלך שתרעה אותי בעולמך ;
וכשאתאיב כן לא יתסר לי שום דנר בעה"ז , דאין הקב"ה מושיע
אלא לאדם שמשמים עלמו כבהמה [קולין דה"ב] : אנל גם
בעה"ב לא אקשר נעלמותי . —

דאם בכחות דשא ירבילכי וגו' , ר"ל אם ייטיב לי בקיי
הנהשמיית שלי , ואם על האחו של הקיים אשיג מאכלי וסקויי וכל לרכי
ברווח ובלי טרקה , או אדע כי רק הוא הרבלבני נתענוגי , ורק הוא בידו
הגדולה על שי שניקות ינהלכי , לא כח ידי , רק כהו עשה
לי הקיל הזה .

ואם כפשי ישובב , וכפלתי בשובנים, ונאקזתי שנלתי הללתה כדנדקה,
ידעתי כי יכתני ב מ עגלי לדק ; דידעתי לדקתו ית' ; דאו שהוא לכקות
כפשי,שבעבור שקטאתי כנדו ית',או נגד בכי א־ס,עוררכ ב ה לשונ יסכלותי

דרוש אור החיים

יאו שהוא לי לנסיון ; או שהוא כדי לשמרני מקטא . דכל זה אני
צוברך להאמין למען שמו היה , שנו נכללו כל ה' האגות
יה"ל , דהיינו שהוא כל יכול ; ושהוא כל יודע ; ושהוא
עלמות הכחכמה ; ושהוא עלמות הבדק ; והמטיב
יהאמיתי ; מכל זה מוכרח שהכל לטונתי חוא כל מה
שקרה לי בעולמי .

אולם גם כי יאלך בגי ללמות , כשאתחיל לבוא אל עמק
העמום של המות , דהיינו כשאהיה מוכך על מטת המות שלי —
יאו עם קלי עיכי הכסבר , אצליך הנטה עליך אבי הטוב — ולא
יבירא רע בהשקתה והתאספפות — ; וזה מג' טעמים .

● ו(1) בידעי כי בכל מקום שאהיה , כי אתה עמדי ; כי כנד
בעה"ז כל עוד שהיה דקקי יותר גדול , כל עוד יותר אתה קרוב
לי ; ולא כ"ש כשאיי בסכנה יעוף — אם הייתי חולה,או התקרבת
לי יותר יחד , וכמ"ש קז"ל [נדרים ד"מ] שכיכה למעלה מטטתו
של חולה ; ר"ל שהאגקה יתירה תהיה או סניב לו.

ואוך לא זהיה ק"ו בן בנו של ק"ו , כשיעוף סניבי ק"ו הסכנה
יהיותר עבומה שאפשר — דהיינו בזמן שהגוף והכפש יתפרדו —.
יאו יתראה עין בעין האב הרקחן לילד שלא המונח בלער — להטיב
כפשו ; וכמ"ש קז"ל [נדה דל"ה] לפכיו יברעו כל יורדי עפר , דכל
אדם בטעת מותו זוכה לראות פכי השכינה — ; וזה כדי להקל
יסורי המות מעליו , כמ"ש באור פכי מלך קיים — ; ואם כן
אם כל כך משגיח הקב"ה עלי — איך אפשר שבסוף תתס הכפש
כהכדוף עטן חכדוף ?

שבטך שרביטו המלכות אשר השטט לי יותר מלכל הברואים , שהכמרתני
בעטרת השכל ; אשר ממני אוביח שלא תתס כפשי במותי, דהכי יאיר לי תכר
יהטהיר הזה בדי לראות בו קטבתי ונלאי הללתי ? ואיה יקכפה
יהבישאה , ואיה יכלתו ית' וטוובתו אשר אין להם קץ ?

ומשענתך , אשר אבי רואה במורגל שבמטך תיסר הרשע גם
בעה"ז ,ותכניעו במדה ככגד מדה , אשר צי"ו ל"א לבכחים כי יזך
עשתה , זאת , דאהבתך הלבדק — ; ואם אקטוב שטס אגוע בעטן
יכו"ו , איה לבדקתך הכפלאה ? כל אלה הס ראיות חזקות בראי
מוצק — זהמה יכקמוכי — ויכיקו דעתי .

ולכן אף אם אראה כי תערוך לסכי טולחן כנד לוררי ,
אם אראה שתעריך טולחכות גדולות לבוררי ולוורריך מטכאיך ה'
אבכא , ויהס בטמקות ירוכו על סעוידותיהס בעה"ז ; אעפ"כ אחטוב
לעלמי כי דטכת בטמן רחשי , כאילו משחת אותו בטמן מלכית,
זהכני בעטני אפרתיי במלך , יולא אעשה בכפי חולה עבור שיחסרו לי

ענוגי האלים שאראה אגל אלו ; וטפי אקטוג כאילו כוסי דזיה,
כאילו כום ישועות שלי חלא על כל גדותיו — .
כי ידעתי בטח , אך טוב וקסד ירדפוני כל ימי קיי
בעה"ז ; ושבתי בבית ה' לאורך ימים,ד"ל וכי אשוב לישב בבית
ה' לאורך ימים עד אין קץ , ואלבכה מקיל אל קיל שם ולא אחם
ולא אתאפם לעולם . —

הנה אחי ! כנד הבאנו ז' ראיות חזקות מאד על השארת הנפש ;
אגל תה.ק חניח על כל אלה פתוקי קומה קודם לה' , באקריה
המאירים בפנינים. וצדיה במגדלות להביק בניה ובת קלב ודנם :
דהאפיקורסים מקליפים פניים לומר לפנינו, שבת"הק לא
נזכר שום דבר מהשארת הנפש ; אבל שעו עיניהם הכהות —
באו אחי וננקפט , דשמא אין סדרה בתורה שלא נזכר בה יחה
העניין ; אגל אינו נראה רק לבעלי עינים, שרוצים ויכולים לראות.
בבראשית. כשהרג קין להבל , קרא לו קול ה' , קול דמי
אחיך צועקים אל י מהאדמה ותובעים נקמה ; ואם נפם הגל
כשלאתה תמה נכרת' , יאין לה קול או קשב ?
בנח כתיב , שופך דם האלם באלם דמו ישפך , ואך את
דמכם לנפשותיהם אדרוש ; ור"ל הרולק את עלמו , אכי
אדרות זה ממנו ; ואם אקר מותו חתם נפשו כעטן , סקי ידרש
הקטא הנורא הזה אקר שכתהווה לאין ?
בלך לך כתיב , זערל אשר לא ימול , הכרת תכרת הנפש
ההיא מלפכי , ואם כל נפש בנאחתה כלא היה תהיה, מה אזהרה
היא זה לאפר ברית ? וזבן שמש בכל סדרא וסדרא , בקשו אחי
היטב ותמלאו בקמטיה הענייין הזה .
ובחנ.ך יש ראיות אלומות אלומות על זה . אמר וישוג העפר
אל הארץ כמו שהיה, והרוח תשוב אל אלהים . אמר, מה
רב טובך אשר לפנת ליראיך . אמר לפזנך תחלא
בטנכם , והכיקו יתרם לעולליהם , אכי בלדק אקזה
פניך אשבעה בהקיץ תמונתיך . אמר, בי לא תעזוב נפשי
לשאול, לא תתן קסיד-יך לראות שחת, תודיעני אורק קיים
שובע שמקות את פכיך , כעימזת בימינך כלח , זעוד
פסוקים רבים , שכולם ינטיחו לבינו שכשתיבו אקר המות תקיד
תקיה ותלך , ותאאר לעולם .

דרוש אור החיים

(ב)

אחר שהבאנו ד' ראיות הנ"ל על השארת הנפש, עתה נ"כ
נחקור איך יהיה מעמד הנפש אחד לאחת מהגוף? ומה שהגבם
של הנבלתי נדיק יוכל לעפ"כ להתאפס אחר מותו? רק קודם לזה נחרן
ביד אלוה ג' קושיות חזקות שיש לנו על קיום הכרת.

דהנה הכרת ילעונו שהות העונ העונג היותר גדול שיוכל לפגום
להאדם, ויתפשט א"ע על גוף ועל הנפש, שניהן יתאפסו לנמרי.
דכרת שבגוף אמרו חז"ל ס"ק [דכ"פא] שמהקוויב כרת מת קודם שישיג
שנת הם'; ושגם בכיו הקטנים מתים. ולתום' שנת [דכה"א],ויבטות
[דב"א] אין בכיו הקטנים שחיו באותה שעה שקטעל מתים, רק
באותן שכאמ' נהן עריריס ימותו, כנועל כדה וכדומה,

אולם כרת שבנבפש ג"כ עונשו מבואר ברמנס [פ"ה מתשונה] שכתב
שכל המקוויב כרת, אחר מותו תתס ותתאפס כפשו ותתהווה לאין;
וכן שמעות בפטות עלת הכתוב הכרת תכרת הנפש ההיא,
דהיינו שיבכרת הוויתה מהעולם, אולם על זה יש יש להקשות:

(א') איזה עונש יוכל לפגום בגוף ונבכים ונכפם, למי שעבר כ"פ
על כרת, הרי כנר בעוינו הנורא הראשון כנר אבד כל הללקתו
בארן ובנטמיס, וגם גופו גם כשמתו כנר מקוייניס להשתקק,
ומה יש לו לאבוד עוד? ומה יהיה עוכשו בארן לטי שעבר
על כות אחר שכנר ענר עליו שנת שנת הם'?

(ב') דאף דאין להקשות ע"פ מ"ש התורה דהמקוייב כרת זרעו
כלה, והרי כראה כמה קייני כרת שאין זרעם כלה? די"ל
דעונג זה מתפשט מעגל להבטה עגוליית של האדם — לפעמים
לא יפגע זה העונג רק לדור השני,או השביעי, הבל כפי כונד מאקל
שנת הקטא, שגלוי רק לשמו ית',

ודבר זה אף שאיכו כראה בדורות ההדיוטייס שאין אדם זוכר
השתלשלותם כל כך; אבל כראה וכרגש בדורות המלכים שרשומים
זרעם ביותר לעיני אדם; דלפעמים היה לשר או מלך ג' או ד'
בכים; ולבסוף אחר איזה מאות שכים תמו נכרתו —; כמי שכראה
לבל קורא נסיפורי [הוועלט געטיכטע]; — זה מפכי שנס אבל
הבלתי ישראלי אפשר קיונ כרת, דהרי ב"כ אוהרתם זהו מיתתן
[סנכהדרין כז"א], ורוב קייני מיתת ב"ד אפי' בישראל, יש בהן
קיונ כרת — ואיך יגרע ב"כ בזה?

אמנם ק' להרי כראה כמה קייני כרת כבועלי כדות, וחקללי
שבתות, וביותר מומרים שעוברים על כל מלות התורה ה ותר
פעורות,ואפ"ה לפעמים מזקיקים וכעשים זקנים ושבים בוכני אשמאי?
וכי ס"ד שק"ו תאמר לנו ת"הק דנר שכראה כל כך הרבה פעבים נהסך?

(ג') ק"ל על הסבנה שאמרה בפי', כל ישראל יש להם

דרוש אור החיים   רעב

קלע"הב , שנאמר ועטך כולם לדיקים . וק' מסי ידבר
התנא , אם מלדיקים , הרי בלה"ג גם קסיי אה"ע יש להם
קלע"הב , זאין חילוק רק בין רב למעט , דהישראלי יש לו שכר
הרבה לקוות כשישמור שלות תורתו , אבל יש לו נ"כ לירא מהפסד
יתר מאשר אומות כשלא יזהר במלוות אלהיו . וח"כ למה נקט
דוקא כל ישראל יש להם קלע"הב ?

אע"כ דגם ברשעי' סיירי ; וכן משמע הלשון , דכל ישראל
משמע אפי' קייבי כריחות ומיתות ב"ד , דהע"ס שקטא ; ישראל
הוא . וק' וכי שחשר שבשמתו מתחפסת וכרתת , היכן נשחר
עה"נ שלו ? מלנד דק' כסי דמסיים ועטך כולם לדיקים , והרי גם
מהרשעים סיירי התנא ?

אמנם חכרי' במדרש[ויקדא רבה ס"לא]על הכתוב *כי אתה תחיר נ'ר'ה'*
חלהי יגיה חשכי , אמר הקב"ה לישראל , בני ! נרי בידך
ונרך בידי , אם אתה תחיר נרי חני מחיר נרך ; ואם אין
אתה מחיר נרי אין חני מחיר נרך , עכ"ל המדרש . וק' מה
הם ב' נרות הללו , שבשנחיר ח' יחיר לנו הקב"ה גם השני ?

אולם נר אלהים כשמת אדם קומם כל קדרי בטן ; דשני
אורות רוחניים הדליק הקב"ה בתוכינו ; הא' הוא הניכוך אלהי
השחיה את כל בניין הגוף וכל אשר בו ; — חה האור הקדום הוא
כביכול חלק אלהי מטעל ממש , כמ"ש ויפק בחפיו כשמת
חיים — כביכול כנופח לנוד , אשר רק רוחו שהוליא הנופח
עמלא את הנוד — .

אולם מפני שזה הניכוך הוא רוחניי דק מחד וחפרתיי , והגוף
הוא עב וגם ביותר , עד שא"א שיתחחדו ב' הפכיים כאלו ויתחגדו
יחד ; לכן נרא הקב"ה ג"כ עוד דבר הממולע בין שניהן , והוא
נפש הבהמיי , או כמו שיקראוהו [נערפפן גייסט] . והוא הוא
הנר הכהה שעל ידו יתחחדו הנשמה עם הגוף ; עד שכל אלה
הג' מחוגגים יחד בדרך בפלא, והיו לחחדים יחד ; עד שהחדם כל
ימי חייו , גם את עלמו לא יוכל לנקם בתוך עלמו ; כי
יקשוב בעלמו שאין בתוכו רק עלם ח' , ושהגוף הוא הכשמה
והכשמה הוא הגוף , כי לדעתו הכל רק עלם אחד .

אמנם כל זה רק כל עוד שחי ; אבל אחר המות ,
תתפנד זאת הקנברה הנחמכה , כמ"ש וישוב העפר אל הארץ כמו
שהיה — והרוח תשוב אל אלהים אשר נתנה . והרוח הזוכר,
הוא הוא הכיכוך הקדום שזכרנו , אשר סיד ה' נתנה להחדם
דמעהיח כחללת כביכול מאלהותו ית' , לכן אינה נח כלי",
וישוב למקורה — .

‹ דרוש אור החיים ›

ארל הנפש הנהמיי המפלוע בין הנשמה להגוף , מפני שכל
תקומותה לא נתהווה רק ע"י הרכבת חלקי הגוף , לכן השכל
נותן שכשיתפרדו חלקי הרכבת הגוף , גם זאת הנפש תתבטל
מפליאות שלה — ; אבל הקב"ה הנטיח לנו שנאם רק כשאור מצוח
אלהינו , גם היה לא תתבטל מפליאותה .

ני *ואלו הם הב' נרות של שבת , שמרמז לעולם שכולו שבת ,
שגם או יאירו לנו ב' נרות שזכרנו ; כי ח' הוא כנגד שמור , הוא
הבלוץ הק יום שלריכים אנו לשמרו שלא יכהה אורו ; והנר הב'
הוא כנגד זכור , שלריכים אנכנו גם לזכור מעמדו ולהגדיל
לו אורו ולהבהיקו — .

זוהו שאמר המדרש כי אתה תאיר נרי , ה' אלהי יגיה חשכי ;
והרי יש סתירה בהפסוק , בתחלה קרא לו שם נר, ותוך כדי דיבור
מכנהו נשם חשבי ?

אלא כך אמר הקב"ה להאדם , נרי בידך, הוא הניצוץ העליון
שתוכל ע"י חטאותיך להחשיכו , אבל גם בירך החשוך דהיינו
הנהמיי , בידי הוא ; אם אתה תאיר נרי העליון שהשקעתי בך
מעולם המכוסא , אם תשמור לי נר זה לבלי לבכלו ולהבהותו
בחטאים , או גם אכי אאיר נרך , הוא רוח הנהמיי שנך ,
שאתן גם לו קיום וחוזק שיתקיים בלאתו מהגוף , שיתקיימו לך
שניהן לעד לעולם .

ני *ובזוה פירשתי שומר כל עלמותיו , אקת מהנה לא
נשברה . דתמוה מחיזה זמן ידבר , אי מקיי הלדיק בע"הז ,
הרי לא לבד עלמותיו רוכה הלדיק שלא ישתברו , הרי גם אם נשרו
עליו יכאב , כמו עליו תאבל ? ואם לאחר מותו , ישווה ללדיק
אם ישנר עלם מעלמיו . וכדקיי"ל באמת [פ"ק דשקלי' מ"ב]
דמותר לשנור עלמות המת לצורך ? ומ"ש בי"ד [סי' ת"ג] דאסור,על
כרחך היינו שלא לצורך — ?

אמנם כ"ל דוזלאי סיירי נשכר עה"נ של הלדיק ; והאי עלם
דנקט קרא , אימו עלם מעלמיו , אבל משמעותו כעולם השמים
לטוהר ; ור"ל הקב"ה שומר כל עלמיותיו של הלדיק , דהיינו
כל מדריגות של הנשמה שלו , כפש , רוח , נשמה , קיה , יקידה ,
ואפי' חלק ח' מקלקי כשמחו לא ילך לאיבוד ; אולם אקת מהנה
לא נשברה , ר"ל אי אפשר שתאצר אחר המות , והיא היה הניצוץ הקדום
והאכוסא שזכרמו דמהיא כלון אלהי ממש כביכול , א"א שיכלה — .

אולם כל זה הלדיק גמור , דאללו אחר יליאת הנפש מתפרדת
החבילה , וכל ח' הולך לדרכו , ורק הבלא דגרמא הנקרא
[קְנָעֲכֶן גייסט] נשאר מקונר בהעלמות ; ואעפ"כ כל מדריגות הנפש

נשארים עומדים עדיין בהשתלשלות רק יחד ובזוהר בשעת המולי"ד או
בט"ו לחודש , או בח"ג , ולבן או נאות ללכת על קבר אבות ,
מפני שאז הנשמה תעוף יותר סמוך וסביב להקנר והעלמות — .
אבל כפ הקוטאת , ח"א שתיכף אחר המות יתפרדו חלקי
הנשמה כל א' לדרכו , ותשוב הרוח לאלהים כמ"ש ; מקמת
שגם הכלוך הקדום הביא עמו כמה כתמים שאירים מקטעלים בנסיעת
הנפש דרך הע"הז ; ועתה לאחר המות כשהיא לבדה לא
תוכל להתנקות , דמקמת רשמותה כשהיא לבדה אינה ויפלת
תחת הזמן של הזיקוק .

לבן אחר יליאת הנפש ישארו משולבים יחד ג' מיני כפשות
הכ"ל,שע"י התיקדותם יחד יפול גם הכילוך הכ"ל תחת הזמן , כמו נקיי
הארבליי , ועי"ז יכול ומסוגל הוא לקנל עכשו י"ב קודש או פקית
או יותר לפי רוב קטאיו , כדי שיזדקקו היטב ; ואח"ר ישונו
שכיהן לישב לפני אלהים , לקנל שכר על מעשיהם הטובים .
[ובן* אמר התנא הדין דין אמת , והבל ר"ל גם החוטא ועכשו בגיהנם , הול
ממותק לסעגוד', כדי שיהא ניאות אחד עכשו לסעגוד' הרוחנית — .
*יוזה לפע"ד כוונת חז"ל נסכהדרין [דסא"א] כשאאל אכטוכינוס לרבי *
הגוף , והנשמה יכולין לפטור עצמן מן הדין, מדא"א לו לקטוח בלתי
קנרת קנירו ? והשיב לו מהמשל היזוע מהרכבת קיגר על
הסומא — כך הק"בה מחזיר הנשמה אל הגוף ודן יחד — .

לא על הגוף מפט הכוונה שיתרכב עם הנשמה , דהרי אנכנו
רוא' הגוף מוכק מושחת ודומם בקבר ? וכ"כ כנראה ב ה ם ו מ יין הידועים,
שהם בין אלבעותינו זה אלפים שנה ? וכי ידוע' שיפה אמר טיטוס
דלקליי' בנורא ולבדרי' לקיטטי' אבב יסי כי היכא דלא לשבקי'
אלדם דיכולחי' ?

רק ר"ל במ"ש שמרכיב הנשמה בגוף , ר"ל בכח הגוף , והוא
הוא הנפש הבהמיי' שאמרכו ; והוא הוא כמו הסומ' שאין לו עין
לנחור מה טוב ומה רע לו ; גם מפני שהוא כסומ' שאוכל ונהכה
מדברי' הארבליי' ואיכו שובע [כיומא דעד"נ] ; וכמ"ש חז"ל אין אדם
מת וקלי טובתו בידו .

והחיגור הוא הנפש העליון שאין לה כח ללכת לבד בג'הז ,
אם לא ישאכו כח הגוף הסומא , ורק הנפש העליון הזה ירואו
הדרך שילך בו , כי הוא הוא הקרבניטא דספניתא . אלו ב'
הכותות יורכבו יחד אחר פרידתם מהגוף כדי שיזדקקו מכתמיהם .
וזהו הטעם של שבעה , ושלושים , וי"ב קודש , שמתאבלין
הבנים על אבותיהם ; כי אין לדיק באריץ שלא יעשה טוב ולא
יקטא ; ולכן כמסר לכו הסוד הזה , שעד אז כמשך זמן
הזיקוק לאט לאט . —

חִדוּשׁ אוֹר הַחַיִים

ולכן משתדלין הבכים או בתי כפס להשתדל להרבות לשנות בזמן ויקף
אנושיהן הב"ל , או ללמוד עבורם ; דע"י שהתעת הביאוס
לעולם , והדריכוס לתורה וליראה , שע"ין ישוו הבנים בתוך זמן
הבוא המעות שעשו,והבי גדול המעשה יותר מהעושה [בב"ב דע"א] מ"ט
יהיה קשור לפני הקנ"ה כאילו עשו האטמת בעלמן מעשי המעלה הב"ל
מידהו כל זה נכל אדם מורגל שפשע לפעמים הבל העונר
על כרת . עכפו יותר כנד — דאף שהכילת הקדוס שאמרכו א'א
שובלה נס למי שמחויב כרת , ויתאפס , עכ"פ ע"י חטאו הכורא יתם
כפאו הנהמיי אקר לאתה , כעכף הככרתמען שאין בהעכף עוד קי ס .

*וזהו שאמר הכתוב הכרת תכרת הכפש ההיא , היינו
הנחמיי עוכה נה, דנעלמותה א'א שתתקיים לעולם מדהיא מורכבת.
אולם כדי שתוזדקק עכ"פ הכשמה העליונ.ה , שכשה"א
לבנדה איכה נופלת תפת הזמן, וא"א שתוזדקק ; לכן כאילאו שניהן
מהגוף , ישאהרו עדיין שניהן מחוכרין וילכו שכיהם יקדו , עד שיתלבן
ויוזדקק הכילון הקדוס יפה יפה — . ואקר מלאות יתי טהרה ,
או תתנטל כפס הנהממיית בכלי אין קפון בו — והכילון הקדוס בעצלמו
ישוב אז ליחוד באור החיים , וקוזר לפחכה שכינה . —

*וזהו שאמז"ל [ד"ה י"ו] דכל קייני כריחות , לאקר י"ב קודם
גופן כלה , ר"ל כח הגוף, שהוא הוא קיי הבהממות, כלה ונאבד
מעליאות ; וכשמתן בערסת , ר"ל שמתלבנת כבדול במוקדה ;
ורוק — ר"ל רוק אלהים קייס,מפזר אפרן תקת כפת רגלי
לדיקים כג"ע .

התבוננו התואר היקר הזה שאמרו חז"ל, שביכו לאוהו חלק של הכשר
שהיא כת כליח , כאילו הוא אפר של עץ הבשרף , שג"כ א"א שיתאפס , אף
שכשה חלקי עץ כלו וכאבדו בהשריף' , עכ"פ האפר א"א שיכלה ;
כמו כן הכשמה אקר שהתלבכה על מוקדה , וכאבד מחנה חלקי
כפש , רוק , עכ"פ יכשב רוק אלהים קייס בהחלק אלוה שב-בכפש ,
להשיני לעודריגה תקחוכה של לדיקים , שישתלמו שכר פצולתן ;
אבל זאת הבת האחוזרת לבת אביה פ'איה ואוכלת כהמ' דכיסופא , ונלתי
ידף פמכה בדק , כי בת מלך היא — :

ולפ"ז מתורץ הקושיא הרא'שוכה שהקשיכו, מה יעבב המקוייב
כרת כ"פ אך דלפי דנרינו , לפי רוב הבריתות שעבר , כן יארך
זמן ויקוקו ולערו קודס שיתטהר הכילון הקדום . ולפעמים כס כזה
מאת שנים לא יהיו די בהם לויקוקו וטהרתו ; וכדהאבהכן בטל"ה
שראה אדם שבכבבם בו רוק קוטף א' שהי' מהראשוכים שהרימו אנן
לסקל זברי' הבכיח ע"ה בני"הפק,וזה הי' יותר מט"ו מאות שכים אק"כ.
וא"כ נס קוש"י שבג"י' מתורלת , שהקשיכו שאבכתנו רוחיס

דרוש אור החיים   רעה

לפשטים קיני כרת מאהיפים ימיט ? דיי'ל דמזדאנכפו רוחים שפי
שקייג ברת כ"ם , סדתה"א לקיים בו עונג אכרת בגופו , מפתלם
זה עב"י יסורי הזיקוק נע"הנ ; כמו כן בענין סיחתו שראוי
להיות קודם זמטו , והרי לפעמי' א"א שיקות קודם ואטו רק
נדרך כם ?

דהנה הק"בה חתס עולמו בגושפנקת דמלבא חותם חטבע
אשר לא ישנהו כל כך בנקל [ועי' מ"ש נס"ד בפרושינו בסדר
נשים דקנו"א] ולכן המקוייג כרת , לשריהו אם
הי' מקבל עבטו שהוקבע לו ; אולם אם יכריח בכף הטנע שלא
ישיגהו העונג ההוא , שימיר היטב נריאותו , וכשיקלה וטט ,
עד מהרה יקרא לרופא סומקה , והוא יתן לו סתים כקיים
שבטבעם סירפאוהו , וכי ס"ד שמאום שוטה זה שקלקל , ישנה
הק"בה טבע עולמו [כע"ז דכ"ה] ?

אלא עיזיא רהטו ורעי' קנירא,אני דרא קושבנא [כתבת דלב"א], דלפי
ענבו שהי' מקבל בעה"ז בקילור ימיו , לפי מדה זו היה קל
ענבו ויסורי זיקוקו נע"הב ; ואשריהו אם הי' כן.

אבל אוי לו להאחר שהפריח ע"י הטבע להבורא ית' כניכול להחליף
עמו , שיקבל הקוטוא עונג נלפי בע"הב בעד עונג עובר בע"הז
שלא היו רק בקילור ימיו ; דלפי אוקד זה יאריך ויוקשה ענוטו
ויסורי זיקוקו בענ"הב , כדי לנקות הכילוך יפה קודס שיכנה
הכר התתכתן הוא נפש הנהתמ"י בקיוב כרת הכ"ל . —

וא"ב גס הקושיא השלישית מתורלת ; דה"פ המשנה ;
כל ישראל , ואפי' רשעים , קייני כריתות ומיתות ב"ד , אם רק
בשם ישראל יכונה , יש לו חלק בנשמתו , שנאות לקבל הזכר
בע"הב , הוא הוא הכילוך הקדום שמסוגל לקיום ; דיהיה איך
שיהי' , זה לנד עכ"פ יתקיים לו , וכמ"ש לעיל. —

אבל נח"הע דוקף לדיקיהם וסיידיהס יש להס קלע"הב ; אנל
רשעיהם, אויני ה' כיקר פרים כלו, בעטן כלו ; 2/3 דרק בישראל יש
בו הכילוך הקדום שאתרבו ; דמ"הט מלטוות ג"כ במלוות וקוקי
התורה שנאותין להשליס על ידן הכילוך הזה על דרך נפלא —
[במ"ש בס"ד בס"ו דפבות דרכ"ו ע"נ] .

ומסיים שפיר , שנא' ועמך כולם לדיקים ; ר"ל אם כל אקד
מהן בכללותו , דהיינו בג' קלקי כאמתו , הם שלמים , שלא
עברו עבי' שעל ידן יתקייב כרת , אז לעולם ירשו ארץ ,
ר"ל מלבד הנלקיית העולקיי' ירשו ג"כ ארץ הגשטי' , ויקומו תקיית
המתים בגוף , בעבור שהכל נשאר להם אז קיים , הכפם הנהתמ"י
והרוקניי' , ולכן בעת תקיית המתים תוכל כל הקנברותא לקוזר
ולפסוע מהלך שלה כנתקלה ,

אולם אם אין לו זכות רק שהוא גלד קטעי , לנעבור שאני,

דרוש אות החיים

נראתיו יצרתיו אף עשיתיו , או לכה"פ מעשה ידי לה תפאר ;
להיינו אף שהנפש הנהפ" כלה בכליתה , וגם לא יקום עוד ,
צחק"הם בגוף , דאיך אפשר לו כן , הרי ספר להתמרוחא ההוא
חזר אחד שהי' מקובל ומחובר הכל ? ואם יקבל נפש בהפיי אחר
אז לא יכיר האדם א"ע או , כי עי"ז התערובות הזר שבניהן ,
יתהוה בריה קדשה ממל ?

אמנם עכ"פ הכילוץ הקדום שבו , תשוב אחר זיקוקה וכפיזלה
לאור נאור ה' , מדהיא מעשה ידי בניכול ; כמ"ש והכשמות א"כי
עשיתי והיא היא עכ"פ תתפאר . נמצא שגם רצע כזה יש לו
עכ"פ בעצמו חלק לעה"ב , לאור נאור החיים .

(ג)

אולם האמונה שגם הגוף ישוב לקיות,זה קשה להשיג בשכל האדם
מאד — ; לא מפני התנגדות הטבעית שנה , דהרי הק"בה אומר
השמכי יפלא כל דנר כאום ה' ? והיד ד' תקצור ? ולכנר יפה
הקשו חז"ל מה דלא הוא הוה , מה דהוה לא כ"ש ?

אבל תמיהתינו הוא לאיזה תכלית יחי' התקום' הזאת ? הכי כל
כך יקר הוא קיי החלום הארלי ,שנקשנהו לתכלית כל התכליתים ?
וגם בתואר הקיים ההיא הקדם , כשתוקף מאד לידע איך
הי' ; הכי גם או נאכל ונשאתה וכקיה כמו עתה , כמ"ש רבינו
סעדי' ושאר איזה גאונים ואעם"כ לא ימות ; וזהו כגד תבלתינו ,
דהרי יהי' לו גוף ממש כמו עכשו, וגם חם אלף שנים יחיה, עכ"פ סוף אדם
למות , ואפי' יהי' לו גוף קשה כברזל על כרחך שתתפיקהו האמן לבסוף .
וא"כ יהי תמוה מאד לא כתב לא דך ולא ך . לא יחי' ולא יחזור
למות ? וכי עניד קב"ה כיסא בכדי ? ונפרטות כס גדול כזה ,
שישוב לקיות אחרי התמו' כדי לקזור למות ? ותו הרי יפה שעה
א' של קורת רוח בע"הב משא לכקות אזיר השכינה מכל קיי ע"הז ?

ותו אם כאמר שאז ישוב למות כדעת גאוכים אחרים דפליגי על
רבינו סעדי' הכ"ל ; זה לא יניח א"ע לתשוב כלל ; דהרי אמרי' בס"ק
[דכח"א] דלחתקזי לי' רב שעורים לרבא לאחר גו'עתו , ואלו
הו"ל למר בערא במיתה ? והשיב דהוה כמשאל בכיתא מקלנא ;
ואעם"כ אילו אמר לי קו"בה דל הדר להאי עלמ' כדהות , לא בעוינא ;
דאע"ג , דיסורי' הקימה א"א שיהיו כל כך מרים כמו שידומה , דהרי
מתנטלת ההרגשה עם המיתה — [וכמ"ש הרופא המשורסים הגדול סולבלאכ
בספרו היקר מאקרמביאהטיק חלק נ'דר 49. 50.] לאעם"כ כפים בעיחוחא
דמיתה יותר ממה שהוא נלעמת ,

ובלחו ספק כן תשיג בנפש כל אדם אחר מיתחו , שלא

מנה את לשוב לעולם הקודם כדי לחזור ולחיות ; וא"כ מה שכך
יש מקומו ? ומה ענינ"ש זה לתלות ברבית וכדומה שאומרים לו
שלא יקום בתח"הם ?

ובכל הקושיות החמורות שהקשינו , אעפ"כ כל איש ישראלי
שבינה בעיקר זה , הוא נתעב ונחלף לפי דת תו"הק בצמדרינה
שלולא עד מאד — ; וכמ"ש הרמנס רים פרק חלק , שכל הכופר
בעיקר זה הוא בכלל רשע ואפיקורס , ואין לו חלק לעה"הב .
ובן אמרי במשנה , ואלו שאין להן חלע"הב , האומר
אין תח"הם מן התורה ורשי ורש כתב שם , דהא שמאמין בעיקר זה ,
רק שאינו מאמין שמופך בן מן התורה , הרי הוא בכלל אפיקורס .
והנאר שבע שם כתב שאינו תלמיד טועה כתב כן בגליון רש' ,
דמה לי אם מכחיש וחומר דהקראי ומיתי הש"ם אסמכתא בעלמא
הן , אם רק מאמין בהעיקר . וכך כתב הרמנס נפ"ג מתשובה
דרק בכופר סכלל וכל בעיקר זה אין לו חלע"הב .

וכפי הנראה רש דייק בן סתתכל מדקאמר הלשון מן התורה ;
אבל לפע"ד דכוונת הסאבה , דהקא בשאומר שאמונה זו טוכך
הפורה מן התורה — נטלא אינו מקודיב להאמין כך — אז הוא
בכלל אפיקורס ,

ואפשר לתרץ גם דנרי רש' , דר"ל דאע"ג דהש"ם סיימי כמה
קראי , דפל אשר עימיס לו , ירצה שהן רק אסמכתא בעלמא ,
עכ"ם יש כמה כתובי שמדנרים שעיקר זה נאר היטב כגון , אכי
אמית ואחיה , מקלתי ואני ארפא ; יחיו מתיך וכנלתי יקומון ;
ורבים מישני עפר יקילו , אלה לחיי עולם ; והמלאך קרא
לדניאל , ועתה לך תעמוד לגורלך לקן הימין . והרי כל מי
שירלה להתעקש ולומר שכל הפסוקים האלו הן רק משל ומליצה ,
הוא בכלל מגלה פנים בתורה שלא כהלכה , ואין לו חלע"הב .
ויהיה . איך שיהי' , חיותינו הוא להשרים באמונה הזאת בלבינו
יפה , בלי לחבוד . ק"ו ע"הב שלנו שקבינו ביצעה גדולה וביוקר
רב ; דחיך קטון כתהווה לנו ולכל ישראל קיית אוסר זה , ואיך נאבדו
כ"כ בנקלות ?

לכן אמרתי לעשות כסת רוק למעלתכם להביא לכם רחיות
נסקום כראוי חולק על אמונה היקרה הזאת , מהקום , והשכל ;
סלנד הקבלה , אשר הסיקן על ג' מיני רחיות הכ"ל כי בי קפק
[ו"ש חם , שבל . קמלה] כמ"ש הדרשנים . ועם ג' סיני זיון אלו
אנקנו כקלן קושים להשמיד כל ספק סלב אדם הקלם .
והלואי שהיינו יכולי' לעשות כן בכלקובות תו"הק , "וכמ"ש
הגנני ונגרה תורתיך ואשמרנה בכל לב , שכשאבין

דרוש אור החיים

טעם המלות יפה ,, או לא יהא לבי חלוק בקרבי . לבכן שעשועי בני
האהובי' — כי מדוטתי . ובן נ.ב.כי אשר חנני ה' חלקק לכם בזה
היום ; השניחו היטב ידידי אחי ורעי שלא יאבד לכם גם שלה
אפת מדבריט — כי בהעניין זה תלוי כל הכלכותכם בזה ובבא .
ונתקור תחלה בזה ב' דברים , (א) מה שהי' ? (ב) מה
שיהי' ? — וכוכיח העתיד מהעבר ; וחעפ"י אחמר לנו לשאל מה
לפנים מה לאחור כרפ"ג דקניג' ? היינו דוקא להסתחכל יותר להלאה
ממה שהורשו לנו קז"ל ; אבל אכנקטו כעלה ובפוץ דק בתקלוכות
שקופים וחטומים שפתחו לנו רבותיט כפי שנמסר לכו איש מפי איש,
וכניא ראיות חזקות על דבריהם הקדושים אשר מיפיהם אבו שותים,
גם מדברי הטנעייס , להורות כתן , כי רות אלהים דבר בם ,

הבי כל דבריהם אמת וצדק .

יאמרינן בסטהדרין [דל"א] חכא דבי אבי , שית אלפי שנין הוה
עלמא , זקד קריב ; חכא כאם שהטביעית מטמט א' לו' שניס , כך
העולם מטמט א' לו' אלפים שנה עב"ל הנמ' . והכי נמי אמרי'
בסוף מסכת תמיד , בשבת היו אומרים, מזמור שיר ליום השבת ,
ליום שכולו שבת ומנוח' מקיי העולמים . זהו הסוד מה שיהי' .
אולם הסוד ממה שהי' , גם זה הראזנו קז"ל צדבריהס
היקרי' , להליץ האור סתוך נקב כמלא מקט סדקית .

דאמרי' בב"ר , ויהי ערב ויהי בוקר [דק' וכי מאחר שלא היה
עדיין שמט בעולם, ערב ובוקר מכיין ? [א"ר אבוה מכר שהי' סדר
זמנים קודם לזה וכו', מלמד שהי' הק"בה בונה עולמות ומחריבן ,
בונה עולקות ומחריבן , ואחר דין הכיין לי ודין לא הכיין לי .

וכדי לאמר לכו הנטה והשקפה עגולית על כל העניין , גלה
לנו רביכו בקיי סוד כעלם בשם המקובלי' במרצת זהר, בפסוק ובנמה
האחץ שבת לה' וגו' , דזה ירמז על סוד כפלא , שיהי' העולם
כבנה ונקרב ז' פעמים , בכנגד ז' שמיטות שביובל , שהם יקד נו"ע
אלפים שנה .

וכחב עוד , שבכל שמיטה ושמיטה הכ"ל , יהי' העולם בנכא
בהשלמה יתירה יותר מנתחיל', עד שלבסוף יחזרו כל כלולי הקדושה
שהוטפעו מהקב"ה בתקילת בריאת העולם לתוך הנשמייס כד
שיטליט א"ע בעלמן ; —ונסוף השמיטה הז' יחזרו מוטלטי' נתבלית
השליקות , לסנה הראשונה ב"ה , כרלוכו ית' — חהר תכלית
כל התבליתים לבריאת העולם . ע"כ תוכן דבריץ שם .

ועל זה רמז לכו קבת גם הרמב"ן , בפסוק אשר ברא אלהים
לעשות ; והרא"בע בפסוק עוד כל ימי הארץ ; והרקק"ט בפרשת
נהר ; שכתב עוד , שלעכיין זה רומזין כמה מלות התורה , שראיתו

שמספר שנע מהגופם והמגולן נכמה מהמלות — ז' ימי שבתא ;
ז' ימי פסח ; ז' ימי סוכות ; ז' ימי כהה ; ז' ימי נקיים ; ז'
ימים קודם המילה ; ז' ימי אבילות ; ז' ימי משתה ; ז' שנים
נטיעה ; ז' שמיטות ביובל ; ז' קני המנורה ; ז' הזאות
ביו"כ — ועוד רבים ;

ובבעלי הסודות הקושי פרקמן שפתחייבו , ושלו' הקפות העולם
הללו , בומז' ז"י נראשית , שכל א' הי' הבכה ליום שלאחריו ,
אחר שידקדקו בהם היטב ; כמו כן בז' ההקפות של העולם יהיה
כל הקפה הכנה להקפה שלאחריו — ושתמיד הקפה המאוחרת
תהי' מושלמת טפי —

וסוד ה' ליראיו , שנמסר להם שאנקנו בעת בהקפה הד' ;
שהוא לפי סדר שבת ימי בראשית הכ"ל כנגד יום רביעי — שבו
העמיד הק"בה המאורות בעולם ; ולבן גם בהיקף זה , עלה אור
תורה הוא השמש המאירה מקנה ארץ ועד קנהו — הוא המאור
הגדול — שאעפ"י שבעו"ה כבוד האומה הקדושה ירד' מאד —
אבל ת"הק תעמוד כשמש נהירה בתמלעית האופק , על שכל
האומות , אפי' אותן שמולאין א"ע לבלתי מקייבין לשמור שלותיה,
כנולרים וישמעאלים כולם יכשאוה , יכבדו התורה הקדושה ,
ויכירו אלהותה — והיא בכבודה ועוזה כשמש המאירה בקרניה
לכל באי עולם — ;

אולם זה המחור הגדול לתמשלת היום — ; וגם המאור
הקטן הוא שדל האכושי שמושל בע"הז — גם הוא התכסא מאד
בהקפה ז' — ועוד יתכסא למעלה כישאה שלא יסוער בגבל
האכושי —

ומלבד שנתגלה לנו כל זה טיד ליד נסור — כנר כזכר דבר
זה באר היטב בפסוקים ; כתיב , רוע תרוע הארץ , מוט
התמוטט' ; וחפרה הלבנה ובושה החמה ; ובגלו כספר השמים
אבל לבאם יבול ; שמים כארץ כמלחו והארץ כנגד תבלה ; הנני
בורא שמים קדשים וארץ קדשה .

מכל זה מוכח שיתקדש העולם פ"א אחר שיקרב ; ומה
שמליכו כמה פסוקי' שמדנרים בהיפך מזה, כנן והארץ לעולם עומדת
ועמידיה לעד לעולם ; כל זה הוא רק בדרך גדישות הלשון על
זמן ארוך ביותר , כמו ועבדו לעולם , לעולם בהם תעבנדו ;
ודודאי כל אדם יפסוט שכוונת הכתוב ר"ל רק זמן ארוך — .

ועתה. אחי ידידי ! ראו על איזה נסים אדני ת"הק מונבקי' ,

דרוש אור החיים

כי הפלא הזה שכמסר לאבותינו ורבותינו, והוא נגלהו לנו זה
כמה מאות שנים — שלאחרנו עוד שהטבע נדורת לעיכינו בזמנים
המתוקרים כבאשכבו הנהירה ביותר.

הדהרוח המפותקק שבאדם, בקסן לגלות כל תעלומות, חתר
וחפר וחפס כחולד נקרבים של האדמה נהל'ים היותר גבוהים
שבעולם ; נהררי [פירקנעען], ותקאולפאלסיסען געביורנע, ותהרי
קאר־ללען נאמעריקא, ונהרי היסמעגלוי נגבול בינא — קפלו
וקפרו שכולן נתהוו ע'י סדרי פלעי' כורחים שעונקים כאילו הובלב
נלי סידור זה על זה נצא תוק וכורא, ותלויים תלולים זה על
זה על רוחב שערה — עד שלא ישוער שכתהווה כזאת רק ע'י,
[וופלטען רעוואלללפטליסען] שהי' פעם ח' על ידו ית' הגוער בארץ
ותהפהך כרגע. —

עוד לא הספחספו זה כ'א גם קחוו במעמקי ארץ ובקרביה —
איאם שאות קלאבסאר עמוק תחת פני העליון של הארץ ; קפו
בצערג וערק, ומלאו תוך עוני האדמ' ד' סדרים וכל אחת
למעלה מקנירתה — כל א' מין אדמה אחרת, ובין סדר לסדר
מונכי' נרוחים שנתקשו וכתהוו נתוחרם לאבן — אשר שם הובינו
שהארץ נתהפכו פניה כנר ד' פעמים.

והברואים שנין שורת אדמה לקברתה, מלאו תמיד שאותן
שמונקים בשורה התחתונה שבחרן, הם בכויים בגודל ענקיי יותר
מאותן שמונקים בשורה שלמעלה מהנה ; וכמו כן אותן שמונקים
בשורה השבי', עדיין יותר גדולים מאותן שמונקים בשורה
השלישית ; וכמו כן מהשלישית להרביעית העתחיי; אבל לפי
גודל הברואים שבכל שורה תקתונה יותר מאותן שבשורה שלמעלה
ממנה, כן יתרחה עוד שלימות היופי בבניינס של הברואים
שנמלאים בכל שורה עליונה, יותר מאשר ירחה בבניין הברואים
שנמלאים בשורה שתחתיה —

עוד כתבו העבעיי', שיש כמה הוכחות בטבע, שהחרן
קבלה פעם ח' דחיפה כוראה מקרן מערבית דרומית לקרן מזרחית
צפונית, אשר ע'יז נקרנו ונבדדו כל פני הארץ. —

וכן מלאו בשנת 1807 למספרס,במדינת [זינעריען] בקלה לפון של
העולם תחת הקרק הכוראח אשר שם תמי7,פיל ח' גדול מחד בכטו ג'
או ד' פעמים מאשר כמלאנו עתה, ושוסי עצלמתיו עתה עומדים
בנאללללאגנישען מחעאום בפעטערסבורג.

ולאשר בהמדינה הכ'ל לפי נודל קרירות התמיידי השולט שם,
אינו מקום גידול פילין, מזה מוכח שע'י דחיפה הכ'ל שקבלה
הארץ, וכצדדה וכנבללה, הולף לשם או הפיל הזה בהמין גלים ;

אז שפעם א' הי' טבע האקלים ההוא אם , בכדי סימוק
לגדל סילין — .

וכ"ב ימלאו במעמקי ההרים היותר גבוהים בארץ , קיות
הים אשר נתקשו והיו לאבן — ; וקכם אקד קוקר טבעי קוסיער
שמו , כתב שמכל ע'ק מיני קיות שמלאו בתקתיות הארץ יש מהן
ס"ק סיכין שאינכ נמלאים כלל בעולם העתיי — .

וכבר ידעכו מעלמות קיה ענכי קתת שנמלאת בעמקי ארץ
מבינ עיר בקלטימקר באמעריקא , אשר ארכה י"ז רגל , וגבהה
מכסות רגליה הראשונים עד קלה כתסותיה , י"א רגל , ומסף
רגליה האקרונים עד גנה, ים ט' רגל . וגם בקיירקפק ובהאקרך
געבירגע נמלא במעמקי ארץ עלמות ואת הקיה , פזורים קתת
הנה ואקת הכה ; וקראו בשם לכל מין קיה כזאת מקמטוט ;

ובן סלאו מין בריאה אבכיית שקראוה איגוחקנקדקן שנגבהה ט'
רגל וארכה עד ל' רגל ; וסתוך תבוכת אבריה שפטו התובכיים
שמאכלה רק קליר ה' . ועוד מין קי' אקרת מלאו שקראוה
מעגקלקזויררום , שהיתה רק מעט קטן מקיגוחקנקדקן , אבל היתה
קי' טרקת . ואוכלת בשר .

מבל האקור נראה ברור שכל מה שמסרו לכו המקובלים זה
כמה מאות שכים, שכבר ה' עולם פ"א ושוב נקרב וקזר ונתקוים, זה
ארבע פעמים , ובבל פעם העולם התגלה בשליקות יתירה יותר מנתקלה,
הבל התבורר עכשו בזמיכו באמת ולדק .

והוחאמינו אקי, שסוד הכפלא הזה ככתב באר היטב בפרשה
הראשונה שבתורתינו הקדושה — לא בה כולה בה ף כי היא
היא אם כל קי .

התבונני רק היטב בין אור קמטיה — בראש התורה נאמר
בראשית ברא אלהים את השמים ואת הארץ — . דתמוה
אם שמים ורקיע דבר א' הן , הרי לא נבראו הרקיע עד יום
ג' ? ואם שמים דבר אקר הוא, דהייכו האיר הדק העליון תנקרא
קטהער , וכמ"ש קז"ל דשמים נוטריקון אש ומים , מלקד שלקק
הק"בה אם ומים ובללן זב"ז עכ"ל , והרי כן הוא באמת האויר
העליון הכ"ל מסולק מרטיבות וקמיסות — ; אבל רקיע הוא שגב
דבר אקר דהייכו האויר התקתון העשוי לכשיסה , הנקרא
קטסקסקטסערא והוא עולה עד ז' וק' פרסאות מהארץ .

עב"פ ק' לסה לא כזבר בתורה שאמר הק"בה יהי שמים כמו
שלוה יהי רקיע ? וקת"ל סזכתהו מקסס , לא היה שייך , על סי
ילוזה ; עכ"ם לסה לא כזבר בתורה בריאת הד' יסודות אש רוק מים עפר ?
ותו כתיב והארץ היתה תהו ובוהו ? זה הקרא קיותר לנקרי,

דרוש אור החיים

דמי לא ידע שקלוס שנראה הקב"ה כל ברוחי הארץ וגם אזר לא
הי' עדיין , א"כ פשיטא שהי' הכל תהו ובוהו וחושך .
ואתו כתיב ורוח אלהים מרחפת על פני המים , זה הפסוק
אין לו פי' כלל ; — רצי פי' כסא כבוד מרחף , כיונה המרחפת
על קנה — ; הלח זה הפי' שהביא רבינו יותר עמוס מהקרא
עצמו . — ולריך פי' לפירוש ?

— אמנם פה גלתה לנו תורתינו הקדושה טפח מהסוד הנפלא
שזכרנו , שאין העולם פה בפעם ראשון , וסבבר נבראו הד'
היסודות נהקפות הראשונות ולכן לא נזכר' בבריאה העת"י
וזהו שסיפרה התורה , בראשית , ר"ל בהתחלות כל
התחלות , ברא אלהים את השמים הוא הטהער , המקיף
כל קלל העולם הנראה , ואת הארץ , הוא כל כדור
הארץ — . אח"כ יתלנג התורה על כל הקריות שנתהוו
בסדרי העולם הקדום . שאין נפקא מנה לנו השתא' בזה כלל — .
אבל סיסרה לנו והארץ היתה תהו ובוהו וגו' , ר"ל
קורה וכתהוה קריבה ושומטה , וכמ"ש בתרנום יב"ע , ולארעא
הות לדיח ורקניא מבני אכשא ; שכוונתו שלא כקרבה וכתבלה
הפליאות לגמרי , רק סע"י רכון עליון ית"שו' , קנלה דקיפה
וכתבלנלו סדרי הטבע הקדום באש ובמים , וכתהווה חושך ע"ס
תהום — .

ואמר שוב ורוח אלהים מרחפת על פני המים — הוא
הוא הרוח הסקיה הכל , המזכר [ניחזקאל ל"ז] כדכתיב מארבע רוחות
באי הרוח ופחי בהרוגים האלה ; הוא הרוח הקיים שנזכר אחר
פבור פרעכות המבול , כדכתיב ויעבור אלהים רוח על הארץ
ישוכו המים ; הוא הרוח המזכר אצל בריאת אד"הר , כמ"ש
ויפח באפיו כשמת חיים ; הוא הרוח שנזכר גם כאן ; ור"ל
שרוח קיים התקיל לרקף ולהדוג על פני המים שכיסו הארץ .
וזהו מ"ש קז"ל בס א כנוד , ר"ל הרוח המקיה הכל , שהוא
נקראח כסא כנוד , כי על ידו יג א: כנולו של ממהק"נה —
זהוא הוא כח הטבע,התקיל לרקף על פני המים — כיונה הסרקפת
על קנה — ר"ל להוליח אפרוחים — — .

ומתחלת התורה מעתה לספר סדר הבריאה העתי , שכל
יום הי' הכנה לקבירו כמש"ל — , דכמו שכל הקפת עולם התחלי' ,
הי' הכנה להתהקפה שנתהווה אחריה — כמו כן נכל הקפה עלמה
היה מעשה כל יום הכנה ליום שלאחריו . — והדברים ארוכים , ולקנר
אכחמו לריב' בזה עכשיו , לבלי להתרחק ממטקוי העכיין .

אכן , הסתכלו אקי הטובי' גדולת התורה ורומחותה הנפלא
השניחו הב' הגדולה , שעמה מתחלת התורה ; והשקיפו על הד'

אחרי שכל הב' הזאת — ונאמר לנו מהמקובלי' שהד' תגין תרמוז
שבעבר ישנו העולם הד' עם כל בריאתיו ; והב' הגדולה
תודיעינו שהגדול שביצירה , הוא כפס האדם השכלי' — כבר
ישנו פה פעם ב' . —

ולפעי'דנ שאותן הבני האדם שהיו בעולם הקדום שנקראין סרי'א
שרפאלדעמיטעמ בל'א , ר'ל הבני אדם שהיו בעולם קודם בריאת אדם
הראשון העכשוי ; הן הן התתקע'ד דורות שנזכרו בשבת [דס'חם
וסניגה [די'ד] , שהיו נבראים קודם בריאת העולם העתי' .
וצא וקשוב ; דלפי דברי רז'ו שם , דרש כן סדכתיב דנר
זוה לאלף דור , שהי' ראוי שתנתן התורה לסוף אלף דורות
הקודמין , דהיינו בתחלת העולם העתי' , שננרא בהשלמה יתירה
בהשכלה ובמדות יותר מעולם שקדמו ;

והרי כל דור לפעי'ד הוא ז' שנים , מטעם שבכל ז' לו' שנים
העולם מאתנה — כמ'ש לעיל בדרשתינו ; א'כ ז' אלפים שנה
של עולם הקודם, הם האלף דור שזכרו קז'ל הודיעונו כאן, שאחר שנתבערו
מהעולם בקולים מכרם ד' כמאות , ונברא העולם מתוקן יותר ,
הי' ראוי שתנתן התורה לאדם הראשון של העולם העתי' , כי
כבר נתבטל העולם כראוי .

רק מפני שהעולם הקדום קלקלו מעשיהן ביותר , לכן קומטו
בלא עת , ונגוועו בעוד שהי' חסר לאלף דורות הם כ'ו דורות
והיינו בסוף תתקע'ד דורות שזכרו קז'ל — ; אשר לפי חשבון
ז' שנים לדור כ'ש לעיל , הי' חירבון העולם ההוא בשנת 5918
מתחלת יצירתו . —

ואותן כ'ו דורות שחסרו בעולם הקודס , חזרו והושלמו
מאד'הר עד מ שרע'ה ; דהיינו י' דורות מאדס עד נח ; וי'
דורות מנח עד אברהם ; וששה דורות מאברהם עד מ שרע'ה ,
שאז נתבטל ונזדקק העולם כבר יפה יפה שיהי' ראוי לקבנת התורה ;
וזהו שאומר הכתוב , מעולם עד עולם אתה אל ;
ונאמר ברוך ה' אלהי ישראל מהעולם ועד עולם —
דהק'בה ברוב רקמיו , בלתי ידח ממנו כדק — ולכן אותן כללות
הקדושות שהושפעו מאלהותו ית' בעולם הקדום , כדי שע'י קפסיות
הבחירה ישליטו א'ע בעצמן ; אבל לבעבור שתושבי הארץ קלקלו ונתהוו
תתקע'ד דורות מקולקלין ומושקתים — והובערו מהעולם — לכן
ברוב רקמיו קוהר ומביאם לאותן הנשמות להעולם העתי' המתוקן
ביותר — שעתה יהי' להם יותר נקל להשלים א'ע בעצמן כרלוט

דרוש אור החיים

יּתֹ' יֻתֵר מבתחלה. — . נֶהְיֵינו דְקָאמַר קְרָאֵי רַבָּנָן יַרְהַעוּלָם עַד עוֹלָם אַתָּה אֵל , רַזַ"ל הַשְׁאֵחֶינִך בְּדִקְמֵיךָ בְּאָב לְבָנָיו חָלֵוֹיכוּ מֵעוֹלָם לְעוֹלָם תָסִיד . לְהַדְרִיבִם בְּמַעֲגַל צֶדֶק ; וְכֵן כָּתוּב כִּי זֶה אֱלֹהִים אֱלֹהֵינוּ עוֹלָם וָעֶד הוּא יְנַהֲגֵינוּ עַל מוּת , רַזַ"ל כְּאָב אָרוּלָה לְהַרְגִיל בְּנוֹ הָעֶלֶם הַרַך , שִׁיתְרֵגֵל לֵילֵךְ לְבַדּוֹ , לָכֵן יַעֲמִידֵהוּ לְפָנָיו בְּמֶרְחָק קָטָן — [הַיְינוּ כִּוֹחַן שֶׁל הַקְפָה ד' נָטוּלִם]— וְיִסְנַב בִּזְרוֹעֹתָיו סָנִיב לוֹ. שָׁאָם יַט לִפּוֹל, יִפּוֹל תּוֹךְ אֲרוֹעֹתָיו ; וְשֶׁאָב יַעֲמִידֵהוּ מֵקָדֶם בְּמֶרְחָק כַּנַ"ל — בָּךְ תְּנַהֲגֵנוּ מֵעוֹלָם לְעוֹלָם , וְתַשְׁלִימֵנוּ בְּכָל ד' מֵהֶן , שֶׁוַּז שֶׁעָט מֵעַט יוֹתֵר וְיוֹתֵר , כְּדֵי שֶׁנָסוּף כָל סוֹף נִקְרַב אֵלֶיךָ .

עָתָּה אֵכִי כִּסַפְתּוּ לְבּוֹ קְלַיּוֹת אוֹר יוֹתֵר בְּעֵיקָר הַזֶּה שֶׁבַּחֶתְוַיָּה ; בְּנַר הָיִינוּ פֹה כֻּלָנוּ בְּעוֹלָם הַקְדּוֹם — וְנִתְעַלְמִכוּ עִם קוּרְבַּן הָעוֹלָם — וְכִרְגִים מִכְּמָה רְאֵיוֹת , שֶׁעוַד בָּאכוּ לְכָאן עִם לְבוּש גּוּף קֶדֶם , יוֹתֵר מוּשְׁלָמִים מִבַּתְחִילָה — ; וְשׁוֹוַ יָבוֹא אֵת שָׁאֵקֶר שֶׁכֻּלָם מִשָּׁלֵוֹת הַיַּם הַקָּטוּב בָּעֲ"הָז , וּבְהַעוֹלָם מִכָּל עַיִן בְּמִיחָתִינוּ — וְשֶׁוַב בְּעוֹלָם שֶׁנִבְרָא אֵחַר הָעוֹלָם הַעֶתְחָי , כְּקָאוֹר שׁוֹב לְהַתְרָאֹת בְּהָעוֹלָם , יוֹתֵר וְיוֹתֵר מוּשְׁלָמִים מִשַּׁל עַתָּה — כַּמַ"ש וִילִיוּ מֵעִיר מֵעִיר כֶּבָבָב הָאָרֶץ — וְכֵן נַאֲחַר וְאוֹרֵק לְדִיקִים כְּאוֹר כּוּגַה , שֶׁמְקִיף יֻתְחֵר נַמְקִיף הָעוֹלָם , הוֹלֵךְ וְאוֹר עַד כְּכוּן הַיּוֹם — הוּא בְּנַף הַקְפָה הַשְּׁבִיעִית , שֶׁהוּא הַיּוֹבֵל הַגָּדוֹל , שִׁישוּבוּ כָּל הַבִּיפּוֹלוֹת שֶׁקְּדֵישׁוֹת לְהַסְנָה הָרִאשׁוֹנָה יְתְ' , בְהַשְׁלָמָה יְמִירָה — חֹהֲוֵי תַּכְלִית כָל הַבְּרִיאָה . —

אוֹלָם אָס עַתָּה בָּעַ"הָז עֲדַיִין לֹא כַּתְנַשֵׁל שִׂכְלֵינוּ כְּרָאוּי לְהָבִין סוֹדוֹת יֹצְקֵי הַתּוֹרָה , וְגַם מִכְּמָה לְדַּדִּי כּוּכָל רַק לְשַׁעֵר בְּהַשְׁתַּעְרַגָּרִים עֲסוּם שֶׁמַבֵּר הָיִינוּ פֹה ; אֲבָל בָּעוֹלָם הַבָּא-חֲבַטְיקִימוּ הַאֵמוּנָה הַזֹאת ,, שֶׁתּוֹכַל לְהַלֵּיךְ וְלִרְאֹת עִם עֵינַיִם יוֹתֵר בְּהִירוֹת וּמְאִירוֹת — כָּאוֹלָם בְּעוֹלָם הָעֶתְחָי עַ"י הַשְׁלָמַת הַשֵּׂכֶל יֹתֵר מִבַּתְחַלָה, כְּגַר כָּל אָדָם יַעֲ"סַע-וְמִּדְבִּרֵים מַה רָאוּי לוֹ לַעֲשֹׂת בְּקִיוּנָיו לְקָנִירוֹ , וּמִבֵּין הַיְטֵיב כָּל דִּינָיו הַטֹּבְעֵיים ; לַעַ"ל כְּעוֹלָם הַבָּא , יִהְיוּ עֵינָיו בְּהִירוֹת כַּי מְאוֹרוֹת הַגְּדוֹלִים מֹשֶׁהֶן יָבִין גַּם כָּל סוּדוֹת הָעוֹלָם,וְכָל קוּקֵי הַתּוֹרָה בְעַצְמוֹת וּלְּחוֹין , יֵאָס יְתַּקֵן וּמָה יְקַלְקֵל לְעַצְמוֹ עַ"י כָּל אֵלֶה — ; גַעַד אֵת הַנֶּוֶנָּעָה לָבוּ , שֶׁאֵז בְּעוֹלָם הַבָּא הַהוּא , כְּה' יְכוֹלִים לְהַזְכִּיר אֵת עַצְמֵיהוּ-יֶהָ , אֵיךְ שֶׁכְּבָר הָיִינוּ פֹה , וּמָה עֲשִׂיכוּ , דְבֵרוֹתָה — וָהוּ אֵמוּמֵא בְּחַיּוֹת הַמֵּתִים .

וּלְפֵעַ"ד וָהוּ יֵמֹר' שֶׁל הַקְדִּים שֶׁאוֹמְרִים אַחַר קְבוּרָה , אֵקֹר צָדֵר טוֹעֲנִוּ הַגּוֹיִיב שֶׁאֵמֹו קִי מְסַתּוּרֵי אֶרֶץ — וְכֹר שְׁבְרוֹאֵי

כל זאולא יחיאשו מהתקוממות הגוף שנ בקיים,ונס כדי לחזק לבנות ישראל
הראשונים נתקרית הפת״ס,לכן יעשדו האבלים בצבאן , ריקראו בקול
יתגדל ויתקדש שמיה רבה .

הנה ב׳ קלות אלו גדול וקדוש , פירושם הוא הפכיי ;
דגדול , ר״ל הוא דנר המתפשט ומתרחב , על שנם בהרי
עינים יראהו ; אבל פי׳ קלת קדום , הוא משם בהיפך , דר״ל
דנר המוכזר וסופרט וגעלם מעין כל ,

אמנם לפי דת תה״ק ואמוגתינו היקרה , לדיך להאמין שנ
בהק״נה ב׳ מדות אלו ; דהיינו (א) שהוא רם ונשא קדום ונעלה
שאד עד שלא ישוג שום בריה ; (ב) שאף שהוא נישא ונעלה
וקדום , אפ״ה הוא נמלא בהשגתו בכל עבייכינו ועניכי העולם
ונעכייני כל הנבראים אפי׳ עם היותר שפלים , לפי רוממותו
ענותכותו ; וכן כתוב , כי רם ה׳ ושפל ירצה , תגוה
ממרקק יידע .

אולם אע״פי שקייני׳ אבכנו אבכנו להאמין כך , אין אנו מביגים
דנר זה בע״הז בנירור ; דאף שעולם קדושתו והעלמתו ית׳
ידעכוהו היטב, כמ״ש כי לא יראני האדם וחי ; אבל מליאותו
אללינו בכל עבייכינד , ובכל מקריות האדם רק על ידו ית׳ הם
כמ״ש חז״ל הכל בידי שמים וכו , זה לא נוכל להשיג בקולר שכליט ,
רק נאמין כך — .

אולם עי״ז יהיי גם פך יקום לכל קושא כי יקשוב שכל מה
שלא ישתדל בעצמו לטובת עלמו לא יוכל להשיגנו ; ונכל מה שישיג
בעולם , יאמר אל לבו כחי ועולם ידי עשה לי הקיל הזה ; לכן
יירף אחר כל עוכג והרווח׳ לגוף , ולא יקוש אם יהי׳ באופן
האסור או המותר .

ולכן כל קיילי מעלה ומטה כולם יהללו את שם ה׳ וקרא את
אל זה ואמר קדום קדום קדום , ר״ל מופרש ונעלם הוא ית׳
בכל ג׳ עולמות הידועים , האכרלי , והגלגלי׳ , והמלאכיי ,
כולם שואלים ז״לו איה מקום כנודו , כי לא ישיגו עלמותו ית׳ ;
ואפ״ה הפלא ופלא כי מלוא האָרץ כבודו ; ר״ל שעם עולם
רוממותו והתעלמותו , אפ״ה וכל מחסיכים שהשגתו הוא מקלח
כל קללי העולמות בגופכי ורוקכי . —

☞וכן כתוב זה שוטד אחר כתלינו נהעלמה , אעפ״כ משגיח מן
קלונות,ר״ל אם קלמת ההללקה סתוקים עליט הוא הוא המשגיח עלינו ;
אבל גם קלח מן הירכים, כאהבכרודים ארוים בחסילת הלרה, מניך
עליהם , משקיף מתוך בקע לר שבכותל ארוקה ואינו כראה ;
כך נס יתי ישגיח או על האדם בעין קשלה להקל לראתו ולמחק

פירוש אור החיים

מרירותה בכל האמרי — שבל האדם לא ירכבו , ויתבות כי אך כ' רואה עליו חן — .

אולם בעולם שאחר תחיית המתים אז יתגלה כבודו , ועין בעין יראו כל בשר וישיגו אלהותו ית' ; עד שאמ"ל בבעימות לשנם הכשילו את העמוד הגלגלי ההוא למקול [נתתביית לע"פ] , אבל אחד מרכבה נאבדבו עליו ית' לומר הכה אלהיכו זה , קוויכו לו , נגילה ונשמקה בישועתו , שכתן לכו תבטה נהירה כזאת — ועי"ז נכבל סליבך בדרך תועה , וכשיג ג"כ יותר לנקל הגלתקיים האמיתית הכלכ"ת — .

וזהו מה שמבשר בעל הקדיש ואומר , יתגדל ויתקדש שמיה רבה , אשר לפמ"ד חיבו תפלה , רק בהלגעה ורטייח כחשה לאבלי רזח ושבורי לב — ; . ויקרא בקובל , אסי' ! אל תלטערו על שטמבנו אלו האחרים הקדושים לפקלון לארץ בסתר — כי בעת אשר ליעקוב , שזה הכטומן עכשיו שוב יקום ויקי' בהרווחה, יתירה ; כי יבוח עת שיתגדל ויתקדש , שמו יתברך , וישיגוהו הכל עין בעין — . ומתי יהיה זה ?

בעלמא דעתיד לאתחדתא , שתתקדש בכשר בעוריה , ולאחיה מתיה בגווה ר"ל בעולם הקדם ההוא , יקומו ויקיו המתים ; והבריאה הקדשה ההיא של הברואים,יהיה כדי לאסק קא יתהון לקיי עלמא , ר"ל שע"י שיקומו ויקיו שוב בעולם המתוקן, יהיה נקל להברואים להתבשא ולעלות ולהתקרב בסוף , כל סוף לסבות כל הסבות ית' , שהוא הוה קיי של כל העולמים — .

וכל זה כאמר ג"כ נקדים הפשוטי שנסוף כל תפלה , שהוא והלי דרך תפלה ; אבל כאמר גם בסגנון אחר בקדיש הפשוט ההוא ונאמר , יתגדל ויתקדש שמיה רביה בעלמא דנרא כרעותיה , ר"ל יהי רלון שתתפרסם עולם קדושתו והשגחתו גם בעולם המקתלקל העתי' שנראו כרלונו כך [כמו שמברכת האשה שיצבני כרלוני, ר"ל אף שלפי דעת האדם היה אפשר שהבריא יותר לטהר , כן יעלה ברלוכו ית' הכבוב מישכל אנושי] ; וזה יהיה בקייכון וביומיכון נקיי דכל בית ישראל , בעגלא ובזמן קריב וכו' .

א"ב מתורלים כל קושיותיכו שהקשיתיו בתחלת דבריו - בזה העכיין . דהקושיא לחיזה תכלית יהיה תק"הם ? י"ל דהייכו כדי שתועלם הנפש או ביתר שאת , והרי זה , אי אפשר בעולם העתיי , מקתת שלא כתבשלה עדיין בריאת העולם כראוי ; כמ"ל שבכל הקפה יושלם העולם בהשלמה יתירה יותר מבתחלה

בתנופסכיות ורוחניות הטעורדים ומתעללים יחד — שי״ע סלד תפלה
לספאן שערם אד״אצ בחפילא פלר עץ בצפת אב ה אבל את צעולם
האדם הנא פרקקו בנוף ובכפל, רהיו טרוזדום וקדמטשיתר
פטה שהי אד״יהר וקרום פטטה.

ומה שהקטצו שנג רולי שוב לקיית ע״ס האדמה למנגך למטול
שאג לעגו פיתה ף אה כבב פורמו לס קה״ל בקהאטר שהפקלם היבו
דרסתיכו זו —., חולם צעטכיהם האדודמת הנבטו יותר להבלאב ש—
דהסכו שתם״בט הדי לחאקרשי — ולאמרנ:

צדיקים שעתיד הקב״ה לבקחזרן, דהייתו בתם״הס, הרבינו
הסמוך ; אעב קזירן לעפדך, שכחטר קדם יאסר לו ,. כל
הכחוב לקייס בידגמלים, מה קהט לעולס קיים אף הן
לעולם קיימין .

זא״ח אותך שכיס שעתיד הקב׳צה לקדס נהן עולמו, דהייתן
בהסרית בעולם דאחמטי, בדי לשוב לקדס עולמו בתח״דם
השני, לדיקים מה הן עוטין בשעת חזורנך העולם
בהוא הכורא ?

הק״בה עטה לחן כנפיס כנטרים — זהו חבל על סדרית
הכפט סהמף נלי לער — בעין עלוית אלהו הבנח למרוס.
שחזרו כל קלקי גופו וכפטו ליסוד הראשון נ״ה ; וכפין שהיה
פרידת הכפט מכל גוף אדם מלא שקטא אד״יהר — ; ומיתה מזה
כימה אז״ל נמקזס אקר ס׳ח ת נב׳ס יק ה דר׳ל ע׳י התשוקה הרנה זהעונג
שיהיה להחוכק חת ולהמפוסק באוחה שעה , להחקרב זא״ן ; לא
יסבול המזושק שום לער עבדידמו — .

וכך יהיה מיחת כל אדם אקר תס״הד , לאר בשמחה ולהלה
יקוו ליום פרידתם , להתעותף ולהחבטף עס כנסי להנה לשמים
בלי שום כאב ומער — שנאטר על כן לא כירת בהאיר ארץ ,
בקוט כהים בלב ימיס .

וזהו שטיס וח״ח יט להס לעס בפרידת הגוף מהכפט כמו
שהוא עכטו ? ת׳ל וקזיי ה׳ ; ר״ל אותן המקחים או לשוב אל ח׳
בשמקה , יקליפו כף שהיה להם בעולם החמיטי עם בח אחד
יותר גדול שיתהווה להם בעולם הבטי ; וניזעם זה ק יעלי אנר
כנטרים ויחגטאו לם בעזוב ונטסקה .

ולנחמה יותר גדולה נס להאדס העתיי , אמרו לכ
הפסוקים שהקדמנו בראש דבריכו — באמור הנביח :
מי את ותראי דל׳ מ את ילד אלהים שתחירא ח״ע ,
כאתראי אכוט יקות , וכאתראה בן אדם קלר יגתן תחת
רגני אדמה ?

מחדש אור נרדים

ס: מִמִּי לֹא תְּבִיא אֶתִי אֶלְמֶךָ ? וְתִשְׁכַּח ה' עוֹשֶׂךָ. וּמִי תַּרְשִׁיא וּכְלִמָּה וְכִפָּשְׁתָּ הַבַּטְתִּי אֲהַכְלִיחַיִּים, עַתָּךְ לְמַעַן מַתָּשַׁת וְחַתָּם ? וַי תַּעֲמִדְ דֶּרֶךְ כִּי שָׁדַּי אֲה' תְּבִיא רִיכוּלִתָּ בְּלִי קִץ, כּוֹמֶה שָׁמַיִם וְיוֹסֵד אָרֶץ ; וְכִי אֵ"א לִי לַנְדוּחַ גַּם לַךְ שָׁמַיִם חַדָשִׁים וְאָרֶץ חַדָשָׁה — ? הָלֹא יִשְׁמֵעֵ שְׁתַשֵׁם כָּל אֶלָה זְתֵם שׁ דָּשׁ מִתַחֵם מִ עֵ לָיִק, דְּהַיְינוּ בְּלִין חָרוּץ בִּלְמֵיי ? וּמִיָּה תֹּאמַר שׁ עָלֵייק ? הֲלֹא בְּכָל מָקוֹם בָעוֹלָם שֶׁתִּתְחַלֵּם הַשִּׂמְחָה, תֵּרְאָה נ"כ שֶׁהָיְתָה הַהִיא הָיָה סִיבָּה לִשְׁחִית אָדָם — .

הֵן אֶפְשָׁר שֶׁיִּסְקִידַךְ מְקַטֵּבַת הַמָּוְת מִקְצָת בְּ דְּבָרִים ; (א) יִסוֹרֵי הַפְּרִידָה ; (ב) אִם מַחֲשׁוֹב שֶׁאַחֲ"כָ תִּתְחַלֵּם.

ג: אֲבָל עַל הָרִאשׁוֹן סוֹמֵר לַךְ , מִ הֶדֶר לְרוּעָה לַהֵבַּתֵּק ; אֵן הַיְסוֹדֵי מִיתָה כָּל כָּךְ קָשִׁים כְּמוֹ שֶׁתַּחֲשׁוֹב ; וְאֵיךְ אֶפְשָׁר כֵּן , הֵרֵי הַמִּיתָה בְעַצְמָה הִיא הַמְנַטֶּלֶת הַהַרְגָּשָׁה , וַהֲרֵי רַק עַ"י הַהַרְגָּשָׁה שְׁנַךְ תַּרְגִּישׁ הַיְסוֹרִים — ; אֲבָל הַקָּבָ"ה יֵסוֹב לְבָלִי חֶלְטְעֵר הִרְגֵּשׁ בְּעֵת הַפְּרֵידָה, וְלֹא יַאֲרִיךְ זְמַן הָעֶצֶם הַהוּא, חָנֵל יְשַׁחֵר לְהַפְּתֵחַ שׁוּסֵרוֹת הָאֲגוּד שָׁבֵּין הַנֶּפֶשׁ לְהַגּוּף.

וְעַל הַיִּרְאָה הַשְׁנִיָּה שֶׁלַּךְ, חוֹמֵר לַךְ נ"כ אַל תִּירָא ! כִּי לֹא יִשְׁמַת לַשַׂחַת , לֹא חַתּוּם כָּעֵד וְשַׁנַּן כָּרוּת , וְלֹא יִמְסֵר לַקְטוּ וְקִיוּמוֹ שֶׁל הַנֶּפֶשׁ אוֹ אֶחָר סְרִידָתָן ח"מַז , אֲשֶׁר תְּקַבֵּל הַנֶּפֶשׁ לָפֶס חוּקָה עָבִית הַשֶׁלַּךְ יַת'.

אוֹ אוּלַי תָּקוּשׁ שֶׁבְּשָׁעַת הַמִּיתָה , כְּשֶׁהַגַּלִּים הַנּוֹרָאִים שֶׁל מַחֲשַׁבְתֵּיךָ יְהוֹמוּ וִירַעֲשׁוּ בְסֵעָר הַפְּרֵידָה , אוֹ אוּלַי אוֹ בַהֲסֵעֵר הַהוּא תִּשָּׁקַע תּוֹטְבַע כְּסָמֵךְ וּמַחֲשַׁבְתֵּיךָ בְיַם הַבֶּהָלָה הַהוּא — .

אֲנִי גָם אֵלַיִךְ בָּסֵם ה' וְאוֹמֵר לַךְ בִּשְׁמוֹ , כִּי אִכְ י ה', רוֹגֵעַ הַיָּם וְמַשְׁקִיטוֹ — וִירַעֲשׁוּ אֵלָה הַגַּלִּים בְּסוּפָה וּסְעָרָה כְּמוֹ שֵׁירְבוּ — אָכִי ה' אֲשֶׁר בְּעֵט יָדֵי אַשְׁקִיטַם מֵעָלֶיךָ — .

כֵּן יִהְיֶה בְשָׁעַת מִיתָתֵךְ , שֶׁלֹּא תִּטְבַּע בְהָמוּן גַּלִּים הַהֵם — וְכֵן יִהְיֶה נ"כ בְשָׁעַת מִיתַת הָעוֹלָם כּוּלוֹ וְהַשִּׂמְחָתוֹ שֶׁיִּהְיֶה קוֹדֵם חַקִּ"הַם עַ"י מַבּוּל אֵשׁ אוֹ מַיִם וְשַׁדוּד כּוֹרֵת , שֶׁיְּקַבֵּל הָעוֹלָם דְּקִיפָה חוּקָה , וְהַכֹּל יֵחָפֵס כְּרֵגַע — פְּדֵי לָשׁוּב לַנְתּ וּלְהָלִין לְקַיֵּם חֲדָשִׁים יוֹתֵר יָפִים מֵאֲשֶׁר עַתָּה .

ה' לְמַאֲוֹת שְׁמוֹ , כִּי הוּא רְצוֹן כָּל הַמַּעֲשִׂים אֲדוֹן כָּל הַנְּשָׁמוֹת , בְאִ"י הַמַּחֲזִיר נְשָׁמוֹת לִפְנָרִים מֵתִים ; וְלָכֵן כֵּר כִּי הָיָה יִחוּד קָהִלָּה קְדוֹשָׁה , וְקִיּוּת וְהַכְלָלָה יְכַתְּרְכֶם בַּזֶה וּבַכָּא . אָמֵן .